THEY WENT TO BUSH

W. B. Collins

They Went to Bush

—••❧❦❀❦☙••—

LONDON

MACGIBBON & KEE

1961

FIRST PUBLISHED 1961 BY MACGIBBON & KEE
© W. B. COLLINS 1961
PRINTED IN GREAT BRITAIN BY
NORTHUMBERLAND PRESS LIMITED
GATESHEAD ON TYNE

TO
MY WIFE BETTE
WHO ALSO WENT TO BUSH

CONTENTS

PREFACE   *page* 15

1 THE BEGINNINGS OF FORESTRY   21

2 PERSONALITIES OF THE BUSH   43

3 THE TRAINING OF A FORESTER   73
   Facets of Forestry   85

4 MAKING A FOREST RESERVE   109
   Farm and Forest   118

5 GUARDING THE FOREST RESERVES   131
   What is Forestry?   146
   The Forest, Cocoa and Man   158

6 MANAGING THE FOREST   165

7 ON TREK IN THE BANDA   173

8 UP DOME HILL   189

9 AT THE CROSS ROADS   201

10 GUARDING THE GAME   208

   INDEX   227

ILLUSTRATIONS

The British Prime Minister in a 'Mammy' chair, Ghana 1960. By courtesy of *West African Review*   *facing page* 64

Surf boats plying off Accra. By courtesy of *West African Review* 64

Old Accra, 1916. By courtesy of *West African Review* 65

Accra today 65

James Town, Accra 96

The Golden Pods. By courtesy of *West African Review* 96

The tangle of the high forest. By courtesy of the Ghana Government 97

Big wood 128

How they used to do it: skidding a log out over the 'corduroy'. By courtesy of the Ghana Government 128

Felling a mahogany 128

A forest ranger's camp in the Bobiri forest reserve. By courtesy of the Ghana Government 129

The bush. By courtesy of the Ghana Government 129

Learner forest rangers. By courtesy of the Ghana Government 160

A hunter 160

The Aframsu Falls in the Bandai Hills forest reserve 160

The end of a forest elephant 161

ACKNOWLEDGMENTS

Many people made this book possible. In particular I wish to thank:

Mr J. S. M. Awesu of Olokerneji, Nigeria, for his most helpful notes on 'Timber' Thompson; J. D. Horne, Esq., of the Forest Research Branch, Nigeria, for introducing me to Mr Awesu; Duncan Stevenson, Esq., sometime Chief Conservator of Forests, Ghana, J. S. Collier, Esq., lately Forestry Advisor to the Colonial Office, J. D. Kennedy, Esq., lately Chief Conservator of Forests, Nigeria, and Alistair Foggie, Esq., lately Forestry Advisor to the Government of Ghana, all of whom helped to perpetuate the memory of 'Timber' Thompson; Mr P. B. Cann-Sagoe retired Forester and Mr E. K. Safo Head Forester for permission to publish their personal accounts on pages 116 and 144; Dr F. R. Irvine for allowing me to quote from his book *Plants of the Gold Coast*; Her Majesty's Stationery Office for permission to quote from H. N. Thompson's *Report on Forests: Gold Coast*; and the Government of Ghana for allowing me to quote from correspondence, reports and the Manual of Procedure of the Division of Forestry.

I wish also to thank: the Government of Ghana for permission to reproduce the photographs taken by the Ghana Information Services; the Editor of the *West African Review* for his kindness in providing me with a wide selection of photographs and allowing me to use those reproduced; Game Protection Officer Basuglo for the use of his photograph, facing page 161; George Cansdale, Esq., sometime Senior Assistant Conservator of Forests, Ghana, for his colour picture reproduced on the jacket, and to my publishers for the photograph of modern Accra. The remaining photographs were by the author.

I am grateful to Michael Harley, lately Conservator of Forests, Ghana, for reading and criticising the manuscript.

'The Prayer of the Trees' (page 140) is believed to be Spanish in origin, its author unknown.   W.B.C.

PREFACE

THIS book follows logically on the theme of *The Perpetual Forest*, my earlier book first published in 1958. In it I attempted a description of that still mysterious, throbbing, pulsating, living entity, the tropical African forest. Here, I have tried to show how the forest in a minute part of West Tropical Africa, Ghana, British Africa's first independent Negro state, was mapped, demarcated and legally secured. I have painted pen-pictures of some of the men whose arduous and lonely lives were spent in carving out the forest estate.

The present generation of expatriate Forest Officers knows little of life in the bush, because it has never had to live in it. The forest estate is now secure and its management is neatly set out as printed plans whose execution is the duty of the indigenous Forest Ranger. The Forest Officer can often inspect from his saloon car and can usually enjoy the comfort of a furnished rest-house, often with electric light and a refrigerator, wherever he goes.

The early and middle-distance Forest Officers lived most of their lives in the bush, in tents, fairly isolated, and rarely had an opportunity of meeting their own kind. They often spent their years in increasingly self-sought isolation. The Forest Officer began as a strong individualist, for the 'social bird' would make a very unhappy forester, and his environment strengthened his individuality. This bred a small race of taciturn, independent and forthright men, their taciturnity emphasized by the fact that most of them were Scots.

They were dedicated men because they had to be. No one who dislikes the forest could possibly live sanely in it for long. Until after the second world war, wives were the exception rather than the rule and spent, usually, only a few months of each tour (normally of eighteen months' duration) with their husbands. Children were neither heard nor seen.

The attractions of such a life are hard to define. It appealed to the outdoor man; it offered great scope for individuality and conferred almost complete freedom of movement and action. No one ever knew to within fifty miles where one's tent would be pitched, and probably only one's Divisional officer cared. Even so, the average young man would probably feel that the disadvantages of almost complete social divorce for most of the year, allied to the discomforts of tent life, outweighed the advantages.

Let it not be thought that these men were recluses or did not enjoy the company of their fellow men. With rare exceptions they thrived in the company of others and revealed themselves to be complete extroverts, yet considered it no hardship to leave civilization for the solitude of the bush, which in West Africa refers to the forest in all its forms.

Throughout the following pages the names of such men as Thompson, Burbridge, McLeod, King-Church and Green, float like nebulae, lacking substance. I cannot portray these men for I never saw them; they had left the Coast long before I arrived, and with one notable exception left no record other than a few cold facts in Departmental reports. The exception was H. N. 'Timber' Thompson to whose epic *Report on Forests, Gold Coast* reference is periodically made and who was the father of Ghana forestry. Though Thompson writes several hundred pages of report it is all intensely objective and throughout there is let drop no hint of the man. What does emerge from the painstaking detail of the report and what can be inferred from the immense pains involved in obtaining his host of facts and the absolute lack of comment on the physical difficulties he must have encountered, is not a picture of the man, but an impression of a personality of unusual strength of character and sense of purpose, one completely dedicated to his task and admirably qualified both mentally and physically to accomplish it.

Mr J. S. M. Awesu, an African living in Nigeria, is perhaps the only man alive who knew 'Timber' Thompson well; he was Thompson's tour clerk over fifty years ago. There are a few retired Forest Officers who served under Thompson but none of these really knew him, though all state that they had never heard or read a single word against him. This is high tribute, for the Coast of fifty years ago tried tempers and patience to their limits and gossip crucified even the zealot. Asked to describe the man Mr Awesu exclaimed: 'Mister Thompson! Ah!' (Coasters will appreciate what wealth of meaning can be contained in that single explosive utterance.) 'When we prepare to go on trek,' Mr Awesu continued, 'he will tell everyone we shall be away for three months, but it is often five months, six months before we return. Mister Thompson!'

By all accounts Thompson was a magnificent hunter and his former clerk confirms this. 'If he was sitting in his office and someone tell him, say, an alligator is in the river, if he was writing a letter to the Governor himself, he will shout for his gun and go and shoot the alligator. If a hawk is flying overhead Mister Thompson can shoot it dead by looking at the hawk's shadow on the ground. He never missed. Mister Thompson! Ah! A wonder full man!'

The Colonial Forest Officer was University trained; he was often a specialist botanist or zoologist as well, always part surveyor and geologist, and invariably an enthusiast. For decades, however, his talents were never fully utilized. Until recent years he was the 'Surveyor Buroni' supervising the surveying and cutting of boundary lines in remote areas and spending most of his other time walking around them, sleeping in a tent and dependent on his line of carriers who headloaded most of his belongings from one end of his District to the other, year after year.

The days of the bushwhacker and his carriers have gone. Forestry is now a printed page, a prescription, a ruled form. Motor roads run deep into the Reserves and what once took a week's hard footslog can now be accomplished in a few hours. The maps are made, the roads are built and everything has a printed schedule. The saga of the expatriate Forest Officer in West Africa has reached its final chapter. The end of this century will see him no more.

Ghana is a small country, roughly the same size as Britain. It is essentially an agricultural country and derives most of its wealth from a single crop, cocoa. For its size, its population of about 5,000,000 (the 1960 census, probably the first accurate census, may reveal 5,500,000) and its state of evolution, it is a wealthy country. In less than fifty years Ghana has passed from a state of complete barbarism to independence. The mass of the people are still comparatively poor and illiterate. Accra, with its international airport, its concentration of taxis (more than any town in Africa!)

and the opulence of many of its inhabitants, gives an entirely false impression. Ghana is still a land of peasants.

In the north the peasants have a hard life and many of them are wretchedly poor. In the forest zone life is easier for here cocoa will grow. It will grow with little attention, a minimum of skill and capital expenditure, and it yields a rich dividend. The cocoa peasant is comfortably off and can send his sons to school. Tetteh Quarshie, a peasant farmer himself, is said to have introduced the first pod into Ghana from Fernando Po towards the end of the last century. From that single pod, it was claimed, stemmed the 8,000,000 tons of cocoa which have since been exported. The truth is less romantic. The Basel Mission brought cocoa beans to Ghana years before the renowned Tetteh Quarshie had ever set eyes on a pod. It was they as much as anyone who set Ghana on the road from poverty to relative riches. Tetteh Quarshie did his bit and his place in history is secure, but let us not forget the Basel Mission fathers, or the men who ensured that the initial efforts of the fathers and of Tetteh came to fruition. Cocoa will thrive only in the forest country where soils are stable, where there is a steady and deep water table, and a high relative humidity. Only in areas dominated by high forest will these essential conditions be found.

If cocoa is to continue to provide Ghana's prosperity, and at the moment nothing else can even remotely be considered as a substitute, a minimum area of forest must be preserved. This book tells how this minimum area was preserved and who preserved it. It tells a little history and outlines a little endeavour, all of which is history belonging to Ghana and deserving a place in the record of this young and virile nation.

The National Monument of Ghana, 'The Arch of Independence', proclaims massively FREEDOM AND JUSTICE. It might also add AND THE FOREST for without the forest neither freedom nor justice would prevail.

THEY WENT TO BUSH

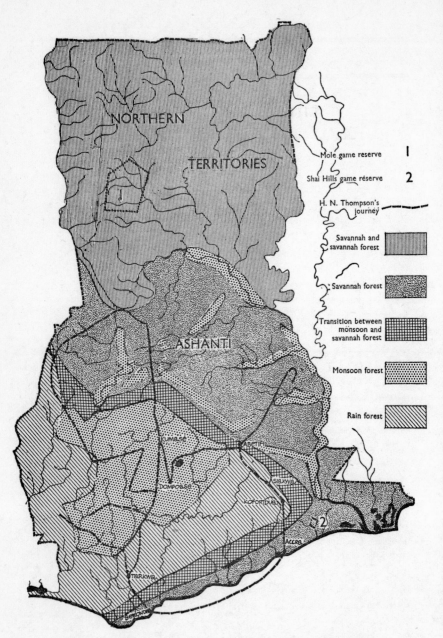

Ghana, showing approximate vegetation zones, game
reserves and 'Timber' Thompson's journeys of 1910

CHAPTER ONE

The Beginnings of Forestry

As the steamer trailed its long, black pennant of smoke across the landscape, Thompson leaned against the teak rail, intent on the the approaching shore. Though he had come this way often, he had previously paid little attention to the low-lying shore of the Gold Coast. On such occasions he was usually dozing in his deck chair under an awning 'taking breeze', with no interest in the monotonous panorama of the West African coastline or the dull life aboard ship, only anxious either to get home on leave, or, on his return, to reach Lagos and resume duty.

By day life aboard was bearable. There was always a breeze in spite of the coalburning steamer's slow ten knots, and if one wished to be alone, as Thompson did, no one bothered except the steward with a glass of orange juice at 10.30 am or tea at 4 pm. Meal gongs were sounded at 7.30 am, 1 pm and 7.30 pm but in the tropics he avoided the oven-like dining saloon and ate on deck enjoying a cold snack brought by one of the stewards. 'Coasters' going on leave were sharply divided into two categories, those who were 'end of tourish' and wanted to recuperate, and those who found the voyage a pleasant and inexpensive way of extending their drinking time! Rather more of the latter than the former would be tipped over the rail as the ship slowly rounded the bulge of Africa, traversing 'the graveyard'. At this stage in the voyage, when the ship was steering a more northerly course with each day that passed between Liberia and Senegal, the first cool breezes that men had experienced for eighteen months brought delight to some and death to others.

The hardened drinkers were the old 'Coasters', the 'bottle-a-day' men who on board ship with whisky at less than 5s a bottle became 'two-bottles-a-day' men and suffered most. Malaria struck suddenly at sober and drunk, judge and clerk, and the good and the bad, the £2,000 a year Resident or the £50 a month miner alike; all keeled over when the bugs reacted to the cool breath of northern seas. A good strong liver, five grains of quinine a day and drinking time limited to a sundowner or two, might keep a man alive when others were being sewn into their shrouds; it all depended on your age, how long you had been on the Coast and where you had been stationed. It also depended on your last infected bite, and your attitude of mind. A man could be a 'Coaster' out to make money (for pay was high and opportunity unlimited) or because he was dedicated to a cause, or a belief, or to the country itself. For some, Africa had an enchantment that the heat, disease, dirt and flies never seemed to dispel. If a man was after money he often tired of the strain of living in a perpetual Turkish bath; he came to hate the Coast and to dread the inevitable separation from wife and children. He brooded and if he didn't actually drink himself to death, he nevertheless died slowly.

Thompson was not an unhappy soul, but a quiet Englishman who kept much to himself, for he was dedicated to his job. He had no joy in the voyage. The greasy, indifferent food nauseated him. The square box of a dining saloon was hot and airless; butter ran like oil, the occasional salads were limp and bitter; there was no fresh food, and even the eggs were addled or pickled. At night those on the starboard side going home found some breeze which kept the tiny cabin liveable. On the port side there was no breeze at all at night. The man who could afford 'Port outward, starboard home' was known as 'posh'. As a civil servant, Thompson was lucky in that he had been given a starboard berth on this occasion.

As the ship drove westwards from Lagos, the seemingly endless narrow beaches unrolled like a backcloth; during the approach to Accra, it, too, seemed at a distance to be just another cluster of mud huts and fishing villages. Thompson peered now and then through field glasses and referred to a map which he had pinned to the rail. Unlike previous occasions he was not going home on leave, he was disembarking. Through his glasses the Gold Coast comprised a broad, flat, scrub-covered plain extending northwards some twenty miles and from which rose, precipitately, the dark, forested mass of the Akwapim mountain range. This extended north-west across the country till it petered out in the furthermost corner of Ashanti. He had marked in pencil the rough triangle of territory enclosed by this high ground, the coast

line and the western frontier with the Ivory Coast. Excluding a
relatively narrow coastal plain of scrub and grass, this triangle
enclosed the entire high forest zone of the Gold Coast, in fact,
some 30,000 square miles.

Thompson clearly saw the southern outliers of the high ground
not far from Accra, and the sharp peaks of the Shai Hills. He had
heard that baboon, oribi, leopard and hyena were common there,
all survivors of a fauna which had once thrived in the forest. As
far as his eye could see, thick forest cloaked the mountains and the
foothills which stretched north-west. He had been commissioned
to inspect and report on this forest. He had brought with him four
pairs of calf leather boots, all hand-stitched and 'broken-in'. In
six months, the time allotted, he would certainly need all four pairs
for the boots of an inspecting officer in the tropical forest rarely
followed known paths. Culverts and bridges were almost unknown; there was virtually no wheeled traffic. Everyone 'footed
it'. A day's journey inevitably meant wet feet even though one
might claim a 'piggy-back' from an orderly, possibly, at the
smaller stream crossings. Wet boots dry satisfactorily only if dried
slowly. A fire ruins them. A 'rotation' of four days was necessary
to keep his boots in a condition suitable for comfortable walking.
An average of ten miles a day in the rough country which Thompson traversed could not be achieved otherwise. Boots and puttees
played a big part in Thompson's life for he was Conservator of
Forests, Southern Nigeria. For years the Gold Coast Government
had been endeavouring to procure the services of an Indian Forest
Officer to advise them on the best means of regulating the hap-
hazard methods of 'exploiting the mahogany forests then in
vogue' wrote Thompson. 'The object was to secure a report on the
forest resources of the country and the measures that should be
adopted for the preservation of the forests against excessive
exploitation.'

Thompson himself refers to the 'mahogany forests'. They were
not mahogany forests, however, any more than they were Cedar
forests or Wawa forests or indeed any specific kind of forest. The
only justification for calling them 'mahogany' forests then was
the fact that only mahogany was being cut, because mahogany
was the only species offered on the market, a trend which was to
continue for several decades. In terms of numbers, only one tree in

fifty was likely to be mahogany. ' Excessive exploitation ' must have meant excessive exploitation of mahogany. Even so, it is doubtful if excessive exploitation was indeed a fact. The market wanted sizeable trees and their agents on the Coast would buy only trees of large size. The felling of undersized trees was unlikely to occur often if there was no profit in it. Up-country contractors might cut undersized trees for a while but were unlikely to continue the practice if there was no sale for small logs.

In retrospect it does not seem that the Government at the time had tried very hard to secure the services of an expert to inspect the forests and advise on their management. Thompson states in his book, ' For one reason or another such an officer could not be found, and it was finally decided that my services should be lent. . . .'

I have little doubt that the major reason was parsimony. No officer of the pukkha Indian Forest Service which commanded the cream of Forest Officers from Britain in those days was likely to be attracted to the ' White Man's Grave ' without a substantial financial inducement. In India, a land whose culture matched his own, he lived the life of a gentleman in a climate which was rarely uncomfortable, enjoying such pursuits as big game hunting, duck shooting, polo, and a social round unknown in West Africa. The Indian Civil Service, which included the Indian Forest Service, had no enthusiasm for West Africa.

The Government's policy of parsimony in Forestry matters was to continue for several decades, but initially, and illogically, it was to pay a rich and continuing dividend : they could not have chosen a better adviser on Forestry than Thompson even if they had offered a King's ransom. As it was, he came on loan at the end of an eighteen months' tour in Southern Nigeria; it cost the Government of the Gold Coast nothing except his travelling expenses.

There was no harbour at Accra and ships anchored a mile or two out. Surf-boats, stout clinker-built double-enders, powerfully driven by a dozen black paddlers seated on the thwarts, unloaded and loaded ships, both passengers and cargo. On very few days in the year is the sea calm off the West Coast. The long rollers begin their majestic sweep shorewards well out to sea, gathering momentum as they travel, with the implacable thrust of three thousand miles of ocean behind them, until they rear in smooth curling splendour and break like thunder on the steep shelving shore. Big ships ride the rhythmic swell with little motion. The thirty-foot surfboats, excellent craft for their purpose, nevertheless sometimes behave like porpoises.

Thompson had often watched others disembarking in the 'mammy chair', enjoying the occasional involuntary duckings suffered by some of them. Now he was the guinea-pig, and the only one! Jamming his coalscuttle helmet firmly on his head he clambered into the wooden box which resembled a double-sided square inglenook. This was slung by a hook from a derrick. His erstwhile companions, homeward bound, some of whom would make involuntary and permanent stops in the 'graveyard', cheered ironically as the donkey engine clattered and hissed and hauled the 'mammy chair' off the deck. Thompson clung grimly to the wooden sides, for there was nothing to hinder one's sudden ejection. The derrick and chair swung sharply outboard and he spun gently thirty feet above the heaving sea. A surf boat moved below him, rising and falling as the embryo rollers passed beneath its hull. Without warning, the donkey engine driver suddenly released the brake, a favourite trick, and the chair fell twenty feet before it was braked to a gentle stop. Thompson managed a wry grin in the driver's direction. The boat boys grinned hugely and manoeuvred their craft gently below the chair, using three-pronged paddles to keep position. The black captain raised his hand as a roller moved glassily beneath the boat; as his craft rose with the water and then slowly began to fall he abruptly dropped his hand : the driver eased off the brake, and chair and boat descended together till the chair sat gently and squarely amidships. Thompson did not know the precise instant when he touched down but as soon as he realized he was safely down he was conscious that he had been holding his breath during the past age-long seconds. Now he released it explosively. On a rough day, 'mammy chair' and surf-boat did not always juxtapose gently or squarely and occasionally not at all, resulting in wettings for the unfortunate passengers. Thompson clambered out of the 'mammy chair' and made his way aft while the donkey engine hissed and clattered and drew the empty box upwards. The boat boys gave way with their paddles and drove the craft steadily shorewards. The early afternoon sun beat down relentlessly. In spite of the constant comings and goings of surf-boats loading and unloading other ships lying offshore, Thompson shut his eyes against the glare, aware that this was more potent than the sun's heat. Ten minutes later the surf-boat grounded on the sandy shore and the paddlers leapt overboard to heave it up.

When the boat was safely out of reach of the breaking surf, one of the boys offered his back to Thompson, who climbed on to it, clasping the muscled sweat-damp neck with his arms and hands and riding piggy-back on the enormous broad back. Africa was a land of strong smells, both of the living and the dead, and Thompson suffered no distaste : he knew worse smells than sweat.

The boy dropped him gently beyond the water's edge. Thompson gave him a threepenny piece, conscious that he was over-tipping him. Threepence was half a day's pay, for which he was rewarded with a cavernous, tooth-filled grin. He strode up the beach towards the long wooden Customs shed. It was the first of January 1908.

Accra was a very different place in 1908 from that which we now see. Some parts of it, however, are little changed, and the dirty tumble-down mud huts which Thompson saw in James Town and Usher Town, still exist. The fishermen of Accra still live there; it is a place of nets, sails and tall masts, and of fishermen making and mending their nets and tanning them, while their women-folk smoke their catches over wood fires. Fish are still dried in the sun, on the roadside and on the banks of the Kawle Lagoon whose stench and filth can only have increased with the years. Elsewhere little of old Accra remains.

The new town of Accra has developed since the second World War, a town of vast, coloured, multi-storied, air-conditioned concrete buildings. Modern cinemas, vast new banks and department stores, touch the skyline. One of the largest and finest hotels in tropical Africa is well patronized. The development of Accra in the twentieth century has taken place in two main phases, both following the two world wars. In Thompson's day it was little more than a collection of mud huts near the beach and wooden bungalows (made from imported pitch-pine!) beyond it on the higher ground still called 'The Ridge'. The Africans, mainly fishermen, lived in the former and the Europeans, civil servants and traders, in the latter. Accra was then, as now, the centre of government. The Governor lived in Christiansborg Castle, now Government House, and Government offices were centred around the still extant wooden club, convenient for the ever-thirsty Europeans. Ever-thirsty because in 1908 there was no electricity, refrigerators, fans or Coca Cola—ice cold. There was no piped water supply and no air-conditioning. Except for the brief period of the rains in July-October, the nights were cruelly hot. The day was bearable with a strong on-shore breeze. As the land cooled in the evening and the breeze fell, the white man sweated. Mosquitoes by the million came out of the numerous lagoons and swamps and attacked black and white alike. The African had acquired an immunity of sorts to malaria through centuries of affliction, though 50 out of every 100 black babies died and half the survivors would die before maturity. The white man had no kind of immunity except that conferred by his daily dose of five grains of quinine. Anti-malarial clothing worn from sun-down onwards kept the flying death at bay, but it also bred claustrophobia, prickly heat and an addiction to strong drink that made the country truly 'a white man's grave'.

After a hard day in the heat, there was little relaxation when darkness fell. There were no cinemas, bars or brothels, the Club admitted only the *élite*; Marconi had only recently invented the wireless. Bed, swathed in a mosquito net, offered little rest till the temperature fell in the early hours. Punkahs were wielded in the houses of the senior civil servants and traders. The rest sweated and drank and caught malaria, or the dreaded blackwater or yellow fevers, for which there was no cure. Of every 100 white men who came to the Coast, ten were invalided or died in their first year! Wives were a rare luxury; it was scarcely a place for a man, let alone his wife, and in any case there was no proper accommodation for them.

There were few cars or even bicycles (which were considered *infra dig*!) and when one shopped or visited friends one usually walked or was pulled in a kind of rickshaw. Living was cheap, however; a chicken cost 9d, eggs were six a penny, and coins worth one tenth of a penny were in circulation. (In the north, cowrie shells were used as money.) Whisky was 7s 6d a bottle and helped some to have a short and merry life.

There was only one small hospital with few facilities and if one fell seriously ill the chances of survival were slight; only the bottle seemed to help and too much of this was fatal.

Outside of Accra, civilization could be found only in the towns of Kumasi, Cape Coast, Sekondi and Koforidua. Tamale, the capital of the Northern Territories, was for all practical purposes as inaccessible as Timbuctoo. Elsewhere the country represented Africa at its darkest. The customs were often savage, human sacrifice and torture were not uncommon, life was cheap, and juju and fetish dominated the lives of the people. Cocoa had only recently been introduced and the standard of living was pitifully low. People travelled little and then only in companies for safety. The death of a chief meant a stool-blackening with human blood and a company of servants to follow him. Solitary travellers disappeared without comment, and their bones would be picked clean by the driver ants. Gold was a common commodity and could sometimes be collected in the main drains of Cape Coast after heavy rain. Disease was rife. There were periodic outbreaks of cerebrospinal meningitis especially in the dry, dusty north, and sometimes it decimated the population. River blindness conferred by a common black biting fly affected thousands. Plague and leprosy were not unknown, while everywhere the water supplies spread dysentery and bilharzia. Malaria attacked all. Although the railway ran from Sekondi to Kumasi and roads were being pushed through the forest in many directions, there was little inducement to travel. Resthouses were few and far between and unless they were obliged to travel, people remained within the safety of their compounds which were, and still often are, designed like miniature forts, for defence. District Commissioners were few and scattered; police were confined to the towns. Law and order by British standards were impossible to impose. The Ashanti wars had only recently concluded; everyone was suspicious of everyone else, but particularly of the white man who strode about wearing what may have seemed to be his badge of office or a symbol of power, the sun helmet.

Land was almost as valuable as blood relationships. The latter were carefully fostered in accordance with long tradition. Land was not sold though it could be leased. Boundaries were known but were marked on the ground usually by streams, trees and bottles. The Stool, representing tribal authority and family unity, welded each of the many tribes into little nations intensely jealous of their rights, traditions, blood and soil. Neighbouring tribes were ready to go to war at the drop of a hat; lusts and passions were easily aroused and were calmed only by copious blood-letting. The annual yam festivals, celebrated in one form or another throughout the country, propitiated the gods of the earth and were excuses for unbridled licentiousness and human sacrifice.

Transport in areas other than those traversed by the Sekondi-Kumasi railway (then spelled Seccondee and Coomassie) was by foot and carriers. In 1909, the Annual Report of the Gold Coast declared that 30,515 headloads of goods were transported by carriers, while 569 bags of mails were so carried northwards from Kumasi. 'No loads were lost in transit, but heavy rains . . . caused delays.' The total revenue from exports, the report says, was £2,655,573, of which timber accounted for a mere £82,937 (volume 820,000 cubic feet). Cola nuts headloaded from Ashanti to the north as far as Algeria brought in £93,850, rubber £263,694, cocoa £755,847 and gold £1 million. In 1958, revenue from exports was £100 million of which cocoa represented £62 million, timber £11 million (32½ million cubic feet) and gold £10½ million.

Into this turbulent and unsettled country Thompson strode, wearing his hand-stitched, calf-leather marching boots.

Half a century ago, a small time in the history of any country, the Gold Coast, which henceforth we shall call Ghana, was a dark segment of the Dark Continent. It was a barbaric jungle hiding practices more bestial and brutal than were known even in Europe in the cruel Middle Ages. In this half-century, however, more has happened in Ghana probably than in any country since the beginning of time. The country's earning power has risen from less than £3 million to over £100 million. From practically nothing the cocoa industry, which today contributes more than half this sum, has become the largest in the world, its plantations supplying more than half the world's requirement of cocoa beans. From equally small beginnings the timber trade has blossomed until it is second only to that of cocoa; 65 million cubic feet of logs were hauled out of the forest and exports of logs and lumber were valued at £11 million in 1958.

Half a century ago, the closed forest zone from which virtually all the wealth of Ghana was and is derived, was, in reality, closed. Agriculture had only just begun to nibble at it. The dense forest covered the southern third of the country in an almost unbroken canopy of leaves, a vast green crown which expressed the fertility of the soil. At that time private ownership of land was practically unknown; land belonged to the people represented by the Stools; it was all tribal land and although the usufruct could be leased and enjoyed the land remained inviolate. There was a little Crown land and a few concessions had been granted to European interests. The outright sale of land, even to indigenes, was unknown; it was a heritage even more valuable than people, for there was an internal market for slaves, and human sacrifice was a common practice.

In Ghana there was no Forestry Department; there were no Forest Reserves, and though the wealth of the country, what little there was, derived solely from the forest zone, the forest itself represented a dark enemy to be destroyed as fast as man was able. Because trees grow slowly and the influence they have on climate, soils, water supplies and on human economy, is not readily apparent, Governments have usually tended to ignore forestry. The Government of Ghana was no exception and for many years forestry was a Cinderella science. In the beginning the Government could not make up its mind what should be done about forestry. Being staffed with administrators, excellent men largely the products of Oxford and Cambridge, it was not astonishing that they nevertheless could see little further than the ends of their elegant noses when it came to practical considerations of proper land usage. For almost half a century the administrators, the District Commissioners, were to wield complete power over the country. In the beginning they failed completely to visualize a pattern of practical usage and even later when practical foresters and agriculturalists were at their beck and call, they failed to implement the practical schemes which were devised to conserve and yet develop the high forest.

The so-called 'mahogany forests' were being creamed as fast as man could get the axe to the trees, but although this was known long before 1907, it was not until that year that something practical was done to control felling. The Timber Protection Ordinance was born of much travail and its enactment gave protection to young valuable trees, making it an offence to fell them below a certain size. Half-hearted, or what appear to be half-hearted, efforts to secure the services of a forestry expert to report on the forests of the country and to advise on what should be done to conserve and manage them, had been made for several years.

Possibly the country's reputation as the 'White Man's Grave' did not attract the right man, maybe, as has so often been the case, the Government was parsimonious. Whatever the reason, it was not until 1907, after decades of uncontrolled felling, that H. N. Thompson, Conservator of Forests, Southern Nigeria —a day's sail away—was 'borrowed' to report on Ghana's forests.

The only way to inspect forests is to *walk* through them. Thompson would have to walk anyway since there were few roads and the railway was only half finished. There was no coast road. Thompson spent six months foot-slogging through Ghana and in that period probably covered more miles in West Africa on foot than any white man before or since. His *Report on Forests*, which was presented to Parliament by command of His Majesty in January 1910, is a closely-printed book of 238 pages and is encyclopaedic in content. Alas, he includes no diary, which would have made fascinating reading. From the map he drew and the routes he followed I estimate that he walked about 2,000 miles, which is an average of over ten miles a day, including Sundays, for six months.

Thompson not only walked, his personal belongings borne on his carriers' heads, sleeping in a camp bed, sheltered by a tent, but he also made copious notes. He gave Ghana's forests the most thorough going-over they have ever had. He does not record how many pairs of boots he wore out, and whether he suffered from illness, or describe incidents and accidents of which there must have been many. His book, close-packed with data, is a cold, shrewd appraisal of the facts. Which was what he was asked, and paid, to produce. The human story would nevertheless have made fascinating reading to the present chair-borne generation.

It is gratifying to observe that within a year of completing his report, Thompson's main recommendation was not only adopted but implemented. Hats off to the Administrators. The Forestry Department after a protracted gestation saw light of day with the arrival of the first Forest Officer of the new Department, N. C. McLeod, Conservator of Forests, who had been Thompson's deputy in Nigeria. Hard on his heels came a new Assistant Conservator, K. Burbridge, who, as Curator of the Aburi Botanical Gardens, near Accra, had accompanied Thompson on his arduous journeys. During the next year McLeod made himself familiar with the country and its forests. Burbridge, having footslogged for six months with Thompson, presumably bought himself more boots and followed.

Fell walkers, hikers and ordinary ramblers think little of walking twenty miles a day in temperate climates. Serious walking in the tropical forest would seem to be the most arduous business in the world to them. It was made harder in McLeod's day by the terrible fear of the tropical sun evinced by all white men. It was believed to be suicidal to expose the head to the midday sun and a cork helmet, a heavy coalscuttle-like affair, was considered a necessity even in the forest. There were believed to be mysterious rays which were lethal or at least conferred madness on their unguarded recipients. This respect for the tropical sun was shown by a very senior Conservator even in the 1950's. The *Gold Coast Handbook*, issued free to every newly-appointed officer, advised one to wear a helmet from 8 am to 4 pm. As the Conservator stepped into his car to drive to the office at 7.55 am he gravely placed his helmet squarely on his head and only doffed it outdoors when his car deposited him at his bungalow at 4.5 pm.

Not only was one borne down by a weighty helmet, but in those early days it was customary to wear heavy marching boots, khaki shirt, ditto shorts down to the knee caps, or breeches and puttees, and to show as little flesh as possible. Buttoned on to the back of the shirt was a thick felt spine pad. The two vertical rows of buttons to which the spine pad was attached were still being sewn on to shirts even as late as 1940 by manufacturers who doubtless made good profits out of spine pads sold to inexperienced Colonial Service Officers like myself.

If the sun smote the head and turned the brain, as I have more than once been told it would without a helmet, what it would do to the spinal cord was too horrible to contemplate! The protection afforded by a woollen vest, a thick woollen khaki shirt, was useless. A boy buttoned on the thick felt spine pad and one went out into the damp gloom of the forest accoutred like a knight in armour. The really careful traveller in boots also wore a cholera belt, a strip of thick flannel wound around the belly! How the early foresters must have suffered. I wasn't born then, but I can recall vividly my physical anguish at having to march thirteen miles through the Ankasa Forest Reserve, twenty-two years ago. I wore new boots, stockings, gaiters, khaki shorts, khaki bush blouse and a coal-scuttle helmet. I was twenty-five years of age and fit. It was my first trek and a horrible one and I never again wore boots or a helmet. Unless it was wet, I did most of my walking in tennis shoes, socks, shorts and shirt and reckoned to be able to manage up to twenty miles a day without great discomfort. There was a standing order in the Department which urged the use of long shorts to protect the knees and obviate tropical sores which several officers had reported to be the cause of their inability to trek. I never had a tropical sore in my life and never saw the inside of a hospital until my trekking days were over.

I sweated easily and in the first few days' walking in the forest I lost about twenty pounds in spite of a daily intake of many pints of water and an appetite which would have shamed a horse. All of it was put back within a few days of returning to headquarters. At the end of a day's trek I could without difficulty wring the sweat from my shirt and vest and I could and often did drink, without pause, three or four pint bottles of water. In the relative evening coolness, after I had wallowed in the tin bath and had my back scrubbed by Kodjo-the-Cook, I drank a bottle of beer. As a thirst quencher I think beer undoubtedly is best. If all else was wasted effort, and I seemed to be one of the few Forest Officers who dis-liked bush life, the gastronomical pleasure of downing that first bottle of beer, 'hot' though it was, a pleasure to which I had looked forward since early morning, visioning it as better men have visioned the Holy Grail, but with the assurance that I would have it in my stomach before darkness, such pleasure made up for the discomfort of wet socks in wet shoes, of thighs chafed red by wet pants, of the fearful effort, which it sometimes became, of reach-ing the camp site which I had selected in advance. If I had earned nothing else, I earned that indescribable few seconds of bliss as I savoured that first beer. With it I killed my thirst; killed it stone dead. I was then ready to enjoy leisurely the second bottle, by which time hunger had utterly routed thirst, and I was ready for a meal, usually by courtesy of Messrs Heinz or Cross & Blackwell, that would send me satiated to bed. I chose the carrier who head-loaded my supply of beer with especial care and watched him as a hawk will watch a mouse.

Then began, so often, the worst part of the day. Temperatures within the forest vary little. The sun rarely reaches the soil but beats furiously on the leafy canopy; the more it beats, the greater the canopy transpires, discharging its cooling water vapour. Below the tree-tops, near the soil, there is little fluctuation by day; the thermometer is steady around the 80°F. mark. So effective is the insulating property of the dense leafy canopy that even when the sun has set, the loss of heat from the forest is so slow that no appreciable diminution is apparent till late at night and then it is rarely greater than a degree or two. But even so small a drop in temperature in the tropics often means the difference between acute discomfort and relative comfort, the difference between waking and sleeping.

Most of my walking was done along Reserve boundaries which are maintained as six feet wide clear lines and are usually easy to follow. The early foresters had no boundaries to follow and not always paths. Burdened by their sartorial equipment they must have suffered.

The tropical traveller who rises with the dawn is foot-weary and ready for bed shortly after sunset, some twelve hours later. Shrouded in the inevitable mosquito net, naked on a thin kapok mattress he tries to woo sleep. With so much water vapour issuing into the air and a constantly high temperature, the atmosphere approaches saturation. The naked body of a man in these condi-tions, denied even the lightest of airs, sweats. His body is con-stantly moist. Prickly heat tickles the small of his back, his neck, inside his arms and legs. He cannot relax; sleep will not come. He fights to sleep and is more awake than ever. The endless stridula-tion of crickets and grasshoppers, the sudden infantile screams of cicada, the screech of hyrax and the continual small sibilance of armies of insects on the move, all contrive to keep his nerves on edge.

When sleep does come, the body temperature falls, sweating stops, and the traveller usually wakes refreshed as the Colobus monkeys herald another dawn with resounding pig-like grunts. Between the wars the Forest Officer spent about half his time in a tent enduring heat, the biting and stinging flies, the discomfort of camp life, the misery of life in a tent in the rains, with no company but his servant, his carriers, and, perhaps, his dog.

The early Forest Officers who established the present pattern of Forest Reserves lived in the bush month after month, enduring the rough life and the loneliness as though they had known no other way of life. Every man may be a Boy Scout at heart, with an innate love of a tent and a camp fire, but there is a limit beyond which camp life ceases to be a pleasure and becomes a burden. Two weeks at a time of constant movement, eating out of tins, sleeping in a tent, with no conversation but a few phrases of pidgin, was about the limit my constitution would stand. The forestry pioneers, among them 'Bertie' Moor, Gordon Greene, Rowney, 'Helen' Wills, Chidlow Vigne, had to put up with it for months on end and did so with cheerful mien. It was their job, but how many of them, and us, appreciated what this job involved when we accepted appointments in Her Majesty's Colonial Service as Assistant Conservators of Forests? A little camp life, hours with gun and camera, cheerful meetings about a camp fire! These were illusions which harsh reality speedily dispelled.

The old ones have all gone now; few left their bones in Africa; most died peacefully in retirement with their families about them. They were dedicated men and they carved their own monuments in Africa, the living Forest Reserves whose boundaries they so laboriously selected and surveyed; monuments as permanent as anything can be, and I salute them.

I cannot speak for other Forest Officers, but during my bushwhacking days, I usually ended the working day in mid-afternoon, sweat-sodden, utterly weary, ready for long drinks and a long rest. While I was ensconced in my camp chair (which I still have) cooling off, savouring the luxury of the day's first cigarette, the biting flies began to attack. As though it were not enough to be tired, and wet and hot! I hated the forest then. This was before the discovery of di-methyl pthallate, 'DIMP' one manufacturer calls it, and the most efficacious means of deterring insects I know. In the early days of my service, fresh from University, with money in my pocket for the first time—as much as I wanted to spend—I strode the forests of Ashanti smoking like a wood-fired locomotive, a tin of fifty cigarettes in the pocket of my bush blouse, and pausing for a drink of squash whenever I felt thirsty, which was often.

Catching a glimpse of myself one day in the mirror in my bungalow, I detected a paunch and, in spite of a full trekking programme, a suggestion of flabbiness. I thereupon began a regime of self-denial. I stopped smoking and drinking during the working day and deliberately set myself the longest treks my carriers would suffer. It was a stupid form of youthful self-flagellation; the denial of liquid refreshment more than once almost de-hydrated me and brought me to the verge of heat-stroke.

I was in no mood to do battle with insects when I slumped into a chair at the end of such a day. The immobile animal is the one which the biting flies attack and man is immobile more than most animals on which these insects normally prey. I have a frightening recollection of Robert (my Corgi) and me being chased out of the Bobiri Reserve by scores of tsetse flies which harried us unmercifully till we ran from that place. Their usual prey is the bush cow or buffalo, which were common in some parts of the Reserve. The tsetse fly is not an easy creature to kill: it has excellent eyesight and a keen sense of smell; it is quick and noiseless and gives a jab equivalent to that from a needle. Unlike the jab from a needle, from which pain speedily recedes, the salivary injection bestowed by the tsetse, presumably to prevent the victim's blood from coagulatings, is intensely irritating and persists for hours.

To smash it before it bites you is almost impossible; it is not easy even when he is sucking your blood, for unless you are very quick he disengages and flies away, watching and waiting beneath the seat of the chair, behind a chair leg, under a table, ready to make another swift, silent dart. Only when he is satiated is he easy to dispose of, making an ugly red splash on the hand. The tired walker sits rigid in his chair, every square inch of flesh protected with handkerchiefs, towels or newspapers. The shade temperature is well above 80°F., he is sub-consciously waiting for the next jab, for no matter what protective measures he takes, the tsetse will pierce man. Sweaty physically: mentally exhausted, and irritated to the point of screaming, one suddenly flings aside all the constricting covers and strides out into the forest, or crawls, defeated, beneath the semi-suffocating mosquito net.

Out in the open plains there is little protection from the sun: the grass is dead; the fire-blackened trees have no canopies. Only along the infrequent stream banks are there avenues of relative coolness, where the air temperature may be as much as 60°F. less than the solar radiation outside, and there is welcome shade. A dry stream bed, with an occasional clear pool, great clean cool slabs of sandstone underfoot, relative coolness and shade. The traveller's haven! A camp chair and table, a month-old newspaper, a drink and a cigarette.

The Simulium fly (*S. damnosum!*) promptly and silently disclaims this. It is another silent fly, small, black, with a painless bite, followed by the most intense irritation compelling frantic scratching. Game and cattle have been driven mad by the bites of this fly which is also the vector of Onchocerciasis or River Blindness. There are other winged menaces of daylight. Among them are the large noisy and aggressive mango flies and the allied kebs, whose bites are not only painful but often induce sepsis and sometimes transmit filariasis, one form of which is elephantiasis.

Night brings the mosquito, both the malaria-carrying Anopheles and the relatively benign Culicids. Protective clothing and light is the answer to these. A good pressure reading lamp will usually keep them away from head and hands, while mosquito boots and long trousers tucked well in provide ample protection against these and a host of other flying and crawling things attracted by the warmth of the human body. As my trekking methods improved, I discarded the kerosene-operated pressure lamp, and utilized electric light from a car battery. This was no greater burden for the carrier than the heavy lamp and its tin of kerosene and obviated much vexatious fiddling with pumps, washers and mantles which invariably gave trouble at the least convenient moments. Anything to reduce the general temperature also was desirable and a 300 candle power lamp gives out a lot of its energy in the form of heat. Later, when the aftermath of war yielded its cheap war surplus, I bought a twelve-volt fan which

ran merrily off the car battery and a tiny Eddystone radio receiver
which with its dry batteries was easily accommodated in a news-
paper-padded suitcase and brought me considerable pleasure. It
was an old-fashioned receiver with reaction tuning. It was thus
possible to compete with some of the screams, shrieks and groans
which emanate from the forest at night. I once interrupted an
ITMA programme coming to me loud and clear in the Banda Hills
in North-West Ashanti, to do cacophanous battle with a pair of
squabbling leopards. The squeals and howls which I pulled out of
that little set speedily quietened them. In the dry season I also
brought my piano accordion along borne in the protection of my
tin bath. The cacophony of the forest soon fails to worry human
ears, indeed an almost silent night is so rare as to provoke in-
somnia. What effect the considerable volume of a 120 bass
accordion played *fortissimo* had on the perpetrators of the forest
howls, grunts and screams, I shall never know. If the effect on the
wild life was anything like that it had on my dogs, one can imagine
the leopards and servals, mongooses and monkeys, retreating
smartly and distantly from the vicinity of my camps, tails
between their legs and howling their anguish at these alien
sounds.

Creatures of the half-light catch the traveller in his most vulnerable moments. Bath-time in the bush should be a period of lazy
relaxation. The oval tin bath, which did duty also as a trunk, was
just big enough for me to lie in with my knees in the air. Often the
water was brown-stained and muddy before I got in. Those
animals which had not been destroyed in the cooking (bath water
was always 'cooked', never heated) died when a liberal scattering
of Pot. Permang. crystals was added. This turned the water a rusty
red but had no effect on the human body other than to stain it
brown. I usually bathed in the late afternoon. Once, making a late
camp, I bathed by lamp light and was stung in a sensitive place
by a large black flying ant, a male of the carnivorous Ponerine
family.

The half-light attracts those light-sensitive creatures, miscalled
the sandflies. These are miniature mosquitoes so small as to be
scarcely noticeable on one's hand, and they breed furiously and
effectively in rotting vegetation. When one considers the supply
of rotten wood and other similar materials which clutter up the

forest, one is not surprised that occasions arise when the sandfly launches its attacks in thousands. Its bite is painless; it is so small as to be practically invisible; it is noiseless. As its salivary injection reaches the blood stream, however, the most intense tickling irritation is set up around each bite, a sensation which may persist for an hour or so, and is the nearest thing I know to the almost exquisite agony produced by *Mucuna*. *Mucuna pruriens* is a climbing weed; locally it is sometimes known as 'Cow Itch'. Judge for yourself the effect on a man of anything that can make a cow itch! I was scarcely out of the boots, gaiters, helmet and spine-pad, stage, when I had my first brush with *Mucuna*. The carriers were cutting a line through scrub and I was a bored and sweaty tail-end-Charlie with the compass and field book. Suddenly there was a commotion ahead and the carriers began to stream back towards me, shouting, cursing and scratching. So close were they to pandemonium and utter rout that the tripod bearing the compass came down with a crash and I caught a clout on the ear from one of the up-ended legs which made me shout. Amid the tumult the theme was 'Apaya'.

'What is this "Apaya"?' I demanded to know when I could make myself heard. The answer was that it was 'some bad ting'. My Twi was too poor to ascertain further and the carriers' English was no better so I determined to find out for myself and against all advice pushed on alone. All I could see at the end of the cut line was a festoon of pea-like pods, each thickly covered with brown hairs. Nothing lethal, dangerous, or even mildly harmful, I decided as I turned, tripped and fell over a stump. My outstretched hands grasped handfuls of hairy brown pods, others lightly brushed my bare arms and knees, face and neck. In the instant, like Kofie Grant's orderly when he touched an electric catfish, I was galvanized. This shock, however, did not cease when I got up and brushed myself down; it went on and on worsening every second. It was not pain; it was as though the nerve ends all over my body were being teased into millions of microscopic threads. I do not think that these sensations could have been intensified very much more without inducing unconsciousness. Cow Itch!

The effect of a mass attack by forest sandflies was in this category, but mild by comparison. It was never possible to determine in advance whether one area of forest contained sandflies or not. Identical areas might or might not breed them. I found out either at bath time, or in the early morning as I sat down to breakfast. They ruined many a breakfast of mine, and destroyed the comfort of many baths. The evenings I have spent, hot and sweaty, irritable with tickling, scratching and shuffling and trying to read a newspaper at the same time.

Similar in habits is the yellow-fever mosquito. Long after prophylactic control of malaria had been secured, firstly by quinine and then by synthetic drugs, the products of coal, itself a product of wood, such as mepacrine, paludrine and nivaquin, yellow fever slew by the thousand. Now a painless injection of vaccine, usually with no after-effects, gives a high degree of immunity to the disease, the virus of which is carried by the mosquito from Colobus monkeys, who live in the high forest, to man. Yellow fever stopped work on the Panama Canal half a century ago; thousands of workmen died, and it was not until the mosquito was controlled by drainage of its breeding grounds that workmen could survive long enough to see the job through. Yellow fever helped to give the West Coast of Africa the sinister name of 'White Man's Grave'. Today, provided that the traveller is inoculated every few years, *Aedes aegyptica* is little more than a scratch fly.

I am sure that something new in the way of biting flies exists in the Ammumuniso area of the Western Region. There I met, only once, what I would describe as a 'fire' fly. Not the light-producing firefly of which a giant variety exists in the same area, as big as my little finger nail, a score of which produce enough light to read by! The 'fire' fly appeared one night of the many I spent in the Forestry Resthouse, and the first intimation of their presence was a series of sudden tiny pricks of fire all over the exposed parts of my body. The sensation was as though minute quantities of hot cigarette ash were falling on me, for the burning sensation lasted only a few seconds. The biters were very minute flies, much smaller than the so-called sandflies. I went into battle with a spray gun, which is an essential weapon for the traveller in the tropics. I never encountered these insects again, nor met anyone else who had.

Bees, though short-tempered compared with their European cousins, have never been any real trouble, though there are bumble bees as big as wrens! In my honey-collecting days during the second world war, while we were once rolling merrily down the Agogo road with a load of honey in clay pots in the back of the lorry, one broke. We proceeded on our way until a gradual darkening of the sky became apparent, as though a dark cloud had floated over us. Indeed it had! A dark cloud of bees! Bees from miles around had been summoned to the feast; there were hundreds of thousands of them.

Swarms of bees have been known to alight in the most unlikely places. A cyclist, quietly making his way along a country road, was suddenly enveloped by thousands of milling bees. A donkey in a field suddenly disappeared beneath a huge mass of hive bees. An engine driver chugging along a quiet country line also received a similar unpleasant visitation. Swarming bees are normally contented bees, usually so gorged with honey from the hive they have just abandoned that they will not sting unless considerably provoked. (It is said that they cannot sting as the distension of the stomach is such that the stinging apparatus cannot be brought to bear.) The bees in the lorry were not swarmers. They were the normal excitable foraging insects. We dare not stop to remove the leaking pot. We dared not go too fast in case we broke more pots. We were, however, able to accelerate sufficiently to lose the bees without losing any more honey.

Hornets are a different race of insects who will not be humbugged. A colony of only a few hundred strong utterly routed us once in the Banda Hills. A carelesssly swung cutlass severed an unseen hanging nest and the next instant all hell was let loose. Our survey party of a dozen or so was, at one moment, a noisy happy throng, in the next, scattered like chaff before the wind. As last man in the line I was last to be attacked and for this reason suffered less than most. If it hadn't been so sudden, and had not been followed by a swift succession of stings (the hornet can use his sting more than once, unlike the honey bee), the sight and sound of it all would have been laughable. As the boys scattered without warning I thought of a lion we had met that morning. I knew what was coming and, like the rest, ran, to little purpose.

My face had the smooth bloated contours of a young hippo that evening, but I could see, talk and eat. There were some whose eyes

B*

were temporarily blinded by the puffiness of numerous stings, and some who could not speak coherently. Those that could chuckled for hours at the memories of those brief painful moments. I was too preoccupied in dabbing on Milton to laugh.

CHAPTER TWO

Personalities of the Bush

But for a certain timidity and caution the late Captain R. C. Marshall CMG, one time Chief Conservator of Forests, would have been a great and much-loved head of Department. I never met his predecessor, the long-lived L. A. King-Church, but viewing their photographs side-by-side one could draw a fair picture of their owners' personalities. Taken at about the same age as Marshall's I should say, that is soon after the retirement age of fifty-five, the picture of King-Church shows a slim, almost dapper, little man, with fine, but strong features, cleanly cut. There seems nothing superfluous or ostentatious about him; his sober lounge suit is well cut, fitting the man.

Captain Marshall at fifty-five looked an old man, retaining the pomposity which he could not help. His white civil uniform with its gold gorgets, and his sword, look new, as though he wore it just the once; it bulks too big for his body. The emblem of the CMG hangs on its silk ribbon from about his neck. In spite of it, despite the half-smile on his face, there is an air of resignation and frustration about him, as though the invisible audience is not giving him the applause he merits. We are what we are; we can develop and improve our characters to some degree, but we live not solely according to ourselves but according to our antecedents.

As I saw him, through the eyes of a lowly Assistant Conservator of Forests, Marshall suffered from a fear of big decisions. As his Deputy, H. W. (Bertie) Moor was the right person for him, for Moor had no hesitation in making decisions and would clearly have loved to implement them. Alas he was fated to be Marshall's Deputy till he retired, a fact which might have embittered lesser men. Marshall's small thin scrawl reflected his caution and timidity; the slow development of his Department reflected those defects more so. The second world war may have been a godsend to him inasmuch as it took the need for big decisions out of his

43

hands. The 'war effort' usurped all considerations of forestry which, by 1939, were becoming paramount, and made it easy to make decisions. Needs were obvious and men like Wills, Vigne, Beveridge and Harper soon devised the means. By the end of the war Captain Marshall was ready to go, and went, diffidently and quietly, with dignity, but to the last not altogether sure that he *should* be going.

To me he was kindness personified, and astonishingly so. Heads of Departments rarely concern themselves deeply with newly-appointed officers. Occasionally, however, he went out of his way to be helpful; he was all encouragement and paternal advice and I was grateful. But his smallness in other things ruined all and it made him just average when he might have been great.

Raging toothache once sent me tearing down to Accra. The ache turned out to be an abscess beneath a front tooth. I refused to have the latter removed and the price of my conceit was the slow and painful drilling of a channel vertically through the middle of the tooth to extract, bit by tortured bit, the living nerve. I could have saved myself this agony for the dead tooth had to come out a year or so later. The Chief Conservator heard of my trouble and invited me to stay with him, an invitation which I accepted with some trepidation. Times have changed and it is unusual for young Assistant Conservators to show the respect for their seniors that we showed a generation ago. There appears to have been a great levelling, if not of intellect and knowledge, of personal approach. Then, the thought of spending my meal times and evenings in close proximity to my head of Department filled me with no elation.

Captain Marshall eked out his food as he did his drinks, with little consideration for his guest's capacities. As a young man I was a considerable trencherman having been reared on the Yorkshire-man's conception of a square meal, in which Yorkshire Pudding as light as a feather is a separate dish and precedes, and sometimes follows, a considerable main course. One Coast egg, two slim biscuits of toast and one cup of coffee for breakfast left me ill prepared for the day ahead, abscess or no.

The Marshalls lived a fairly Spartan existence. The ultimate was not even reached when one morning he complained querulously to Mrs Marshall that he could find only fourteen

matches in his box whereas the previous night when he had gone
to bed he was sure there had been sixteen! The ultimate in
niggardliness occurred on my departure when I was asked by
Captain Marshall how much I paid my washman. I told him
' 15s a month '. He then seemed to be pondering some little problem for there was silence for a moment or two, until he said :

' Then if you leave my washman 2s it will be all right, don't you
think? '

I then realized that my head of Department was charging me
for my laundry. Solemnly I handed over 2s. ' I think that's fair,
don't you? ' said R. C. Marshall.

As a man R. L. Brooks did not appeal to many of us. As an
administrator he was outstanding and he revolutionized the
Department at a time when, failing a revolution, we should have
become just another Department. People who choose their voca-
tions with care, and those who follow their star, come what may,
eagerly, usually do their jobs far better than those who lack the
fire of dedication.

The forester is usually a dedicated man. The Ghana Forestry
Department has often been referred to in glowing terms and its
members have earned a reputation for integrity and devotion to
duty. Even the Administration (they disliked being called the
' Political' though their correct designation was the Political Service) with the frightful condescension which they lavished on
lesser beings, admitted that we had some ' pretty good chaps '. I
even recall Peter Canham, who subsequently rose high in the
Administration, commenting on the fact that I had had some
articles published : ' Fancy a forester who writes! ', as though we
used some prehistoric sign language to inscribe our reports on
slabs of bark! The young District Commissioner was all right until
he stepped off the ship at Takoradi, having put up for the first time
his shining badge of office, which, stuck on the prow of his helmet,
proclaimed him District Commissioner, and therefore not as other
people. It was a sudden inexplicable mental metamorphosis. From
that time on the District Commissioner and his wife evolved
swiftly and immutably into insufferable prigs. There were exceptions and I was privileged to know one or two.

Brooks was another kind of human being seeking efficiency who
seemed to regard a collection of human beings (Forest Officers)

as a machine designed and functioning primarily to meet this end. He was seemingly indifferent to the fact that we breathed, ate, drank, and lived as he did. As head of Department he was much respected, both by those in it and those outside it who watched our progress under his leadership, yet he did not inspire a warmer feeling among his subordinates, for he held himself too aloof. Unlike Marshall he loved decisions, the bigger the better, and directives flowed outwards like emanations from a queen bee, to guide and prompt the workers. More was achieved under Brooks than even we dreamt possible. He laid, and laid securely and surely, the foundations of a Department, already hard-working and enthusiastic, which within a decade was to become almost the efficient machine which he considered it should be. I do not think any group of officers in this period could have worked harder, or were inspired to work harder, than the ACF's and SACF's, both in bush and out. When Stevenson succeeded Brooks, the latter had collected his CMG and was promoted Permanent Secretary in the Ministry of Food and Agriculture. Stevenson in time was awarded the OBE. Thus were the men and the 'machine' honoured.

As a man, Duncan Stevenson was as different from Marshall and Brooks as figured wood is from 'run of the mill'. He brought a fine touch of humanity with him. Marshall was 'Captain Marshall'; Brooks was 'Mr Brooks', but everyone who knew Duncan Stevenson, and he radiated friendship, thought of him as 'Steve'. The popularity of a man can be fairly gauged by the use or misuse of a nickname, and when popularity is allied with efficiency in a head of Department the result is a happy and efficient Department. Unlike Marshall or Brooks, both of whom came from the West Indies, as did Moor, Steve was a Coaster with most of his thirty years service in Ghana, and when he replaced Brooks he broke what we feared was becoming a tradition: a West Indian Service Chief Conservator. We felt him to be one of us, which in heart he was.

My wife and I still retain the fond image of Steve, wheeling our youngest son Michael, on one of his visits to the bush, down the pot-holed Mpraeso road, happily babbling the kind of baby talk which instantly quietened the infant, in order that we might have a few minutes conversation with Mrs Stevenson. Steve had the gift of putting people at their ease. He toured the Districts and spoke with his ACF's, which was more than any other Chief Conservator had bothered to do. He was happy to accommodate them in Accra and lavished on them the kind of entertainment which he, as a bushwhacker, knew they couldn't get in the bush. He established a close, friendly, and in consequence, valuable bond with his junior officers that paid enormous dividends in work and loyalty. When Steve went, it was a sad occasion.

The Brooks era, which was a thin sandwich rich in filling between the Marshall and the Stevenson periods, was the fourth phase in the Forestry Department's history. During the first two decades after 1909, we had successfully fought for legislation to give the Department a status and a meaning. The second phase was the King-Church and Marshall period of consolidation, ending at the outbreak of the second world war with a vast permanent forest estate. The war was waste. The period ought to have been spent devising means to manage that estate, and thereby to fulfil the second major clause of our policy. Even the latter had not been clearly and decisively stated.

Though the war years (phase three) were wasted, I doubt whether we should, under Marshall, have evolved methods of silviculture and systems of management any more quickly even if we had had this period untrammelled by the war effort. It required the cold incisiveness of Brooks to lay down a policy, get Government's approval of that policy, and begin actively to implement it.

At that stage it is sad to confess that no one had more than the vaguest ideas of West African silviculture and management. The excuse that we were fully engaged during the second phase in consolidation is a thin one. We had an excellent Silviculturist (Chidlow Vigne) who, properly directed, could have saved us years of time and Ghana millions of pounds. Marshall, for reasons best known to himself, suddenly ended Vigne's appointment as Silviculturist. Thus it was that at the end of phase three we had the estate but lacked the knowledge to manage it. At the end of that phase we had not one proper working plan; no one knew how to draw up a full-scale management plan for the West African forest.

Phase four, the Brooks era, completed by Steve, was one of forestry effervescence. Means of regeneration of the forest were sought and found and applied. It was a phase that merged almost imperceptibly into the present: as research yielded results these were applied to the forest through the management plans. The culmination lies decades hence but the present phase wherein all production Forest Reserves will have their own working plans is almost completed. Our silviculture and management though effective are still the subject of constant modification through constant research. The handling of the tropical high forest is an interference with nature, an assault on the unknown and techniques will constantly have to be modified as our knowledge of the forest increases. The forest is being subjected to a non-stop treatment whereby each of its five-and-a-half million acres is being walked over, literally square yard by square yard, giving the combined operation parties an unparalleled opportunity to study each plant and each animal within it; to scrutinize each fold in the ground and to observe more closely than ever man has observed before in this environment the progress of natural regeneration upon which the success of West African forestry depends. Man has never before attempted control of so much of nature so intensively.

Alistair Foggie was the last expatriate Chief Conservator of Forests, retiring in 1961. His departure before the end of his contract period will place a considerable strain on an already overstrained Division of Forestry whose professional staff is almost all young Ghanaians lacking in experience. I know that Alistair wanted to stay on to the end of his contract and wished to revise the somewhat unwieldy mass of forestry legislation. This short, thick-set, tough Scot has, in his thirty years of tropical service, a record of fitness which may be unique. Though he may lack the charm of his fellow Scot, Steve, the brilliance of Brooks, or the ebullience of his predecessor, Hughes, he possesses those rare virtues of kindness and understanding. Having served as his Deputy for two years I regard him as the very personification of soundness. He is the canny Scot! Perhaps he has not ruled from the same high pedestal as Brooks or Steve, yet he has imprinted his stamp firmly on his Division and his wide specialist knowledge of management and silviculture has served us well during the most difficult period of the Division's history.

Foggie assumed charge when the fabric of the Department was crumbling. Practically the whole senior cadre had retired in 1955-56, accepting the Government's offer of lump sum compensation and full pension, leaving a thin crust of Conservators below which was a space empty of experience. The influx of young professional Ghanaian officers who had been to England and had been trained in Universities there began in his time and is now in full spate, following independence. The status of a 'been-to' is high in his own country. He is probably a first or second generation literate. His parents are very likely illiterate, living close to the red soil of Ghana, clinging firmly to the rigid family code which is so powerful a force in his country; the individual is less than the family. This form of communism sometimes bears hard on the successful individual, even though his success has been partly due to joint family efforts.

The young 'been-to', wearing his degree like a halo, is now a professional man, an Assistant Conservator of Forests drawing his minimum £680 per annum, a small fortune in the eyes of his people, owning his own car, refrigerator, record player, and housed in a Government bungalow for a nominal rent. These are the outward signs of success. For these, however, he must pay doubly.

He is obliged to help his family, his probably numerous brothers and sisters, even the more numerous cousins, nieces and nephews, in addition to his wife and children, for he is usually married. The glamour of the gingerbread may soon pall. Financially, he becomes little better off than his office boy. His family, in its widest implication, clings closely to him. In days gone by the ACF looked after his District, his forest estate, checking the reports of the Rangers and Guards, living a life on foot and in a tent. Today, with the forest estate under intensive management, he has little time for bushwhacking. The estate which a generation ago had only a potential cash value, is now big money. The unreserved forest is almost destroyed and within a decade practically all exploitation will be confined to the relatively small forest estate, the Forest Reserves where control is rigidly prescribed by working plans. The plans have their own rigid form of control subject to the Chief Conservator's periodic scrutiny.

The exploiters, who for decades have torn at will into the unreserved forest, creaming it to their delight and littering it with waste logs not of the top quality, now find it galling to have their yield of trees prescribed for them in a small given area. Working in the Reserves, as they must, on a rigid sustained yield which includes trees of all qualities and by no means always of the largest sizes, and obliged to pay their silvicultural fees of 7s 6d per acre *in advance*, they must cast avaricious eyes on neighbouring compartments, scheduled for future felling, separated from the present felling area only by a thin cleared line. The Forest Guard cannot be everywhere at once; the Ranger has numerous and widespread duties, and the ACF has 5,000 square miles of District to look after. Prime mahogany commands up to £30 a ton at port; royalties per tree are only a tiny fraction of this. A few £G notes represent a Forest Guard's monthly pay; and not all Rangers can resist a bribe.

The young 'been-to' often feels the pinch. He often manages to 'prang' his new powerful car, for he will probably never have driven before. Repairs are costly and are rarely fully met by insurance. Political influence is slowly widening its scope, and the cocoa farmers, finding it difficult to obtain forest for the continual expansion of their plantations, constantly seek the release of land within the Forest Reserves. To the farmer these are 'Cocoa' Reserves. The farmer is the electorate, and the Government, should it become hard-pressed, or should it be obliged to make unpopular decrees and impose unpopular taxation, may find itself obliged to appease the farmers and de-reserve part of the forest estate. As Nkrumah has said, as his statue outside the National Assembly proclaims, 'Seek ye the political kingdom and all else shall be added to it.' He should know that the destruction of the Forest Reserves will, within a generation, destroy his country's economy and crumble his new-won kingdom to dust.

The tradition of relative honesty built up over many generations in Europe has not had time to mature in Ghana. Until this century, and even during it, life was close to nature. Families lived very much a hand-to-mouth existence, education was almost non-existent, religion was confined to the few towns; children were born in the bush, lived and died in it; the people were small farmers and hunters, only the Chiefs and their families boasted any luxuries (there were a few relatively rich traders on the coast and in the towns). Morality was a family and tribal matter. One respected a neighbour's wife and his property. Money played little part in life, temptations were few, and wrong was often punished summarily by execution.

As business crept into Ghana, born of Imperialism, life became more complicated. To become a successful trader or businessman, one had to be sharper than one's customer or competitor. The delimitation between sharpness and sharp practice was not, and still often is not, clear. If a contract could be broken without consequences, well done! If one could bribe one's way into a lucrative deal, no one thought the worse of it; if one wanted a favour, payment was expected. For wrong-doing, an impassioned 'I beg you' might get one off.

A generation or two of literacy and a few years in a more civilized country cannot be expected entirely to erradicate the loose principles which have actuated much of the business dealing in West Africa. That bribery and corruption exist is common knowledge. The burden of the young professional officer is thus considerable. He is often impoverished by his own vast family and tempted by dealers who offer bribes to get what they want with no compunction whatsoever. If they cannot get it, they are not beyond fabricating charges of bribery and corruption.

The control of a Division whose District Officers are mainly young 'been-to's', subject to the stresses and strains of a newly independent Ghana, depending largely on their technical Foresters during their first tour of duty, is no sinecure. Whereas the Forest Ranger or Forester felt it his duty to guide the young expatriate officer with fatherly care he rarely feels so paternal towards his own countryman whom he expects to 'know the ropes'. Moreover, the influx of these young men coincides with the full implementation of forest management and the maximum exploitation of a comparatively untouched forest estate. With one or two exceptions, all Conservators are also relatively young post-war appointees and their burden is correspondingly increased. To see, successfully, the Division through this, the most difficult phase of its history, will be an achievement of high order. It needed a sober, unhurried, calm character in the chair, and Alistair Foggie was just that.

Foggie was almost passed over when his predecessor, Hughes, recommended the promotion of Beveridge to the vacant Deputy's post over Foggie's head. In many ways Beveridge is 'Steve' over again, charming, sociable and quick-witted, and my wife and I are much in his debt for his kindness to us in the difficult days of our first son's babyhood in the bush. I have no doubt he would have made an excellent and much-liked Chief Conservator. Whether he would have had the stamina to hold on during the present years of transition, frustration and insecurity, *and* achieve the development that is being achieved, I am less sure.

Foggie, hearing of his impending supercession, fought it and won. It was never justified: he had a clean book, longer service than Beveridge, and if of slightly duller quicksilver, should have been an automatic choice for promotion as events have since proved. As these words are written, the white man is fast on his way out of Ghana. In little more than half a century, not counting the first world war years, the Department of Forestry, now a Division of the Ministry of Agriculture, is handing over control to its Ghanaian officers. In that time we can proudly point to a permanent forest estate of a size and disposition which is the envy of many larger and more advanced countries; to a forest policy approved by the Government and designed to protect and improve that estate, and to a system of management which should meet the country's entire timber requirements in perpetuity. This is not a little achievement and I make no apology for emphasizing it. For most of that half century we were a Cinderella service composed of 'Surveyor Buronis' who watched the trees growing. We were hardly ever fully staffed and never given enough money. Our policy and our work were not understood; we were unpopular and largely incorruptible.

We did what was needed unsolicited, and I quote proudly from the American *Journal of Forestry*:

> No nation ever gave firmer support to forestry in lands under their care than did the British. They built up a skilled and dedicated group that is the envy of nations. British foresters were trained and conditioned for work overseas. They had a vision and a technical competence and an integrity that will always command the admiration of our profession. Often they worked under incredible difficulties, yet the monuments they have left in terms of sound silviculture and painstaking research will long endure. But with the transition of the British Empire into the British Commonwealth, it was inevitable that much of the administration would be taken over by nationals.

George Tolmie was one of those unfortunate 'Coasters' who was married and had children. This state is not normally an unfortunate one; but the Coast in his time was not normal. The choice of European married couples who had children to be educated was either separation of husband and wife, or separation of parents and children. Though some would dispute it, the Coast is no place for children once they reach the stage when they should have the company of their own kind. I have worked for almost half my life with and for Africans and have no colour consciousness. Nevertheless I consider it desirable that my three sons should have companions, not necessarily of their own colour, but companions who are following the same educational and social roads. When the time comes for him to develop his or her own social consciousness, the white child should, I think, be in his own country. This inevitably means separation.

In Tolmie's time, in the 'thirties and 'forties, it was unusual for wives to spend more than a few months of their husbands' tour with them; it was almost unheard of for children to spend any time with their fathers. Husbands saw little of their wives and even less of their children. The problem, though eased, still exists. Children and wives can fly into Ghana in a few hours from Britain. Except for very senior civil servants and some executives of commercial firms, one trip a year is usually the maximum possible. The Government and some employers, provide free passages once a year only; beyond that, the employee must pay the £200 flight bill himself. This sum should not be an insuperable barrier between parents and children, but most family men have two homes to maintain, one on the Coast and one in Britain. With this burden and the cost of education at home there is little change even out of a super-scale salary.

Before 1939, though life on the Coast was often hard, monotonous and short, it was not expensive. Professional pay has since risen by little more than fifty per cent. The cost of living, however, has rocketed by several hundred per cent. Fifty cigarettes then cost 1s 3d; a bottle of beer 9d. The same cigarettes now cost 5s, the same beer 2s 6d. An excellent steward boy was then obtainable for £2 to £3 a month; an indifferent one now demands £10 and is as temperamental as a prima donna. A kerosene tin, which everyone used as a bucket, was 3d; it now costs 6s. Then we paid no rent for our quarters; today we are charged between £60 and £150 per annum. In 1939 one could buy a new American saloon car for

£200, or a good second hand one for £30. Then, West Coast pay was the highest in British Africa (how else could the Colonial Office attract the men?); now it is the lowest.

As a young man George Tolmie was 'Handsome George' a tall, well-built fellow, a fine golfer, raconteur and a much liked sociable man. As he slogged and slashed his way through the wet forest of the Western Province, from Insu on the railway towards Enchi sixty miles west as the pied crow flies, George must have thought often of his first child, whose birth 4,000 miles away was now due. The distance on foot was nearer 100 miles by the time he had circumnavigated the tortuous footpaths: a tree falls and because it is often too big to climb over or to cut, the path goes around it; the tree decays, disappears, but the path is never straightened. Trees are always falling and paths wind like serpents.

He had instructed Forest Guard Osumanu to remain at Insu station until the cable announcing the event arrived. He was then to force-march to Enchi and thence to the Yoyo Reserve, which George was to survey and demarcate. The Yoyo is near the back of beyond, near the French frontier, the haunt of Bongo, leopard and chimpanzee, and, some say, the 'little people'. Enchi is still a miserably little village at the end of the road, still wearing a bemused air, as if wondering why it is there!

It rained in the Yoyo, and for three days and nights George was stuck in his tent, fuming impotently at 'the wet', miserable with the incessant drumming of the rain on the outer fly, sick of the mud and the damp and the loneliness. He was awakened on the third night by a large black hand fumbling at him through the mosquito net and a voice adjuring him to 'Wake up, sah; wake up'. It was Forest Guard Osumanu with a cable, damp but readable, announcing the birth of his son, and all well. Gloom was banished, the bottle was brandished and canny Scot though he was with his liquor, a tot went around the tent to each boy and the Forest Guard.

A little after dawn George wrote a cable of congratulations to his wife. The leg-weary Forest Guard carried it uncomplainingly over the rough tracks and delivered it to the Stationmaster at Insu for despatch, a journey which took him three days, and another three days' return journey to George's camp. They did a lot of walking in those days.

Twenty years later, George was a flabby, sagging edition of the splendid figure he had once been. His square jaw had more flesh than it should; nevertheless his features still revealed the classic cut, his greying hair was still thick and wavy and his moustache a thing of beauty. But his colour had gone; where it had been a lively ruddy tone it was now greyish, like his hair, and he had a paunch. As Divisional Officer he was inspecting my District (Dunkwa) visiting the territory he had once travelled over on foot.

George was shortly due to retire and wished to sell his car. Accordingly he was not going to spend anything on it unless he had to, that was obvious, and I looked dubiously at the four smooth treadless tyres he was entrusting to the rough, often jagged, lateritic roads which was all I could offer him. We had over 200 miles to travel together before he returned to Takoradi, a further 100 miles south.

He led in his big Ford; I followed in my Vanguard Estate car. Two hours and some seventy miles later he had a puncture and a petrol stoppage, near enough to Sulesu to push the car into the well-appointed workshop of Messrs African Veneer and Mahogany Exporters. We were welcomed by Umiker and Fluekiger, the one as thin as a rake, the other the reverse. They entertained us with their accustomed generosity and after a superb lunch, well laced with wine, we staggered into the afternoon sun to find the puncture mended and the petrol feed cleared. Firms such as this deserve a recorded word of thanks for they were always generous with their hospitality and lavish with their help. Not long before, when a wheel bearing had seized, the neighbouring firm of Messrs African Timber and Plywood, who subsequently bought out AVME, had loaned me a saloon car to take me back to Dunkwa, had repaired the damage to my car and refused any payment. A dozen miles further on, near the ferry over the river Tano, George had another puncture and we discovered his spare to be flat. There was no alternative but for him, his boy and his loads, to transfer to my car. Overloaded, flat on the springs, we left the Ford on the roadside and continued on our way gingerly to Enchi.

Two miles beyond the ferry we stopped for tea at the Forestry Resthouse at Ammumuniso. Re-unions can be touching occasions.

When the re-union comes after twenty years and is unexpected, even when those re-united are a senior Conservator and an ex-Forest Guard, the occasion is a memorable one. The Ammumuniso resthouse keeper was ex-Forest Guard Osumanu, the very same who had carried the good tidings of George's first-born from Insu to the Yoyo, two decades before. Recognition was mutual and George's usually stern visage lit with genuine pleasure. They almost fell on each other's shoulders.

We drove slowly on to Enchi, being careful to blow the horn before crossing the fetish bridge. Beneath this bridge flows the Amuni stream, reported to be the bathing place of the children of a powerful fetish whose headquarters were within a stone's throw of the resthouse and whose influence extended over a vast area of forest. Not to give the children warning of your approach is to court disaster, even death, it is said. No lorry driver would *dare* to cross the bridge without blowing his horn! I blew to illustrate the story I told George. He was a bit testy when we arrived, maybe the value of his car was less than he had thought. It was dusk and George's boy busied himself with a paraffin pressure-lamp, while I with an air of superiority clipped on a pair of twelve-volt reading lamps to the car battery and ran the leads through the resthouse window. I also plugged in the little fan besides which we cooled off and opened the bar. I travelled with a small ice-chest in which to keep my beer and filter water cold. A refrigerator perverts one's thirst so that a warm drink is so insipid as to be sickly. For the first ten years of my service I did without a 'fridge and people thought me slightly odd when I asked for 'hot' beer when cold was available. The truth was that I didn't like cold drinks and considered, as I still do, that excessive cold numbs the taste buds and detracts from the flavour of a drink. When I married, however, I bought a new car and a new 'fridge and ever since have been a slave to both. When I produced the iced beer George was delighted. We drank all six bottles and regaled each other with part of our life stories. He was astonished to hear that my ambition was once to be a dance band pianist, doubling on the trumpet! I knew all the hit tunes of the 'twenties and 'thirties for I had hammered and puffed them out in my 'teens. We closed our tête-à-tête with dubious renderings of a dozen or so popular ballads which had been our joint favourites. Our harmony was close but not good, but the boys had long since gone to the village and there was no one we could hurt or annoy. We let rip.

I rarely stayed at the Enchi resthouse. Our own at Ammumuniso was infinitely superior. Besides, the mattresses were harder. They were so hard that George got little sleep that night. A rhinoceros' horn is not, as may be supposed, made of horn as in the case of a cow's or antelope's. It is of compressed hair. The Enchi mattresses were also hair mattresses much compressed. George's fifteen stone compressed them further if that were possible. I commiserated with him next morning, not too heartily, for I had slept well. Our visit to the Research Centre near Ammumuniso was rained off so we had hardly used our feet on this tour and George had nothing further to do but to return to Takoradi. In response to a message given to a lorry driver the previous day, Messrs Umiker and Fluekiger had repaired the two punctured tubes of his car. We transferred George's loads from the Vanguard to the Ford and with a wave of hand they drove off. Waiting till their dust had settled, I followed. As a tour of inspection I imagined it had largely been a waste of time.

I never saw George Tolmie again. His wife died soon afterwards and George, with an incipient thrombosis, a grown-up family which soon broke up, found himself as many an old Coaster has found himself, an ageing, lonely man, worn out by Coast life. Like many an old Coaster he did not long enjoy his retirement, and after several violent heart attacks his obituary was sadly written. When I came to the Coast in 1938, people lost no time in acquainting me with the fact, which they maintained, that the average expectation of life after retirement at fifty-five was five years. Judging by the quantity of alcohol and the amount of rich food which the average Coaster consumed in a climate which demands moderation in all forms of indulgence, I was not surprised. At one time this may have been founded on fact and I believe it applied to those Coasters who for one reason or another—it was usually loneliness and/or a thwarted and broken family life—'hit the bottle' too hard.

Captain Marshall aged rapidly after retirement, but it was the effects of gas in the first world war, I believe, which caused his comparatively early demise. King-Church, who retired as head of Department lived until 1958, which according to my reckoning made him a ripe eighty-two, a good age in any climate. 'Timber' Thompson was in the seventies when he died, as was 'Bertie' Moor, and Messrs Gent and Greene were still drawing their pensions in 1958, a quarter of a century after they left the Coast. Clearly, the five-year rule did not and does not apply generally to retired foresters.

The new generation of expatriate foresters (fast diminishing as Africanization proceeds rapidly) the *last* generation of expatriate foresters, are a more sober, mature, and less frustrated generation. They marry young, have their wives and children with them, and no longer have to suffer the rigours of life in a tent. Many of them have never lived in a tent and have never enjoyed, even in retrospect, the freedom of constant movement untrammelled by Control forms and Statements of Account. Their forestry has been brought to fruition and their lives are emptier, though they can never appreciate this smug fact. They have no need to. They are now applying the cool methods of science to the estate roughly hacked out for them by their elders, among them the old Coasters whose memorial is a perpetual living one, created for, and to be regenerated by, younger hands. Those of us who carved out the forest estate have a more personal stake: to each of us there is at least one Reserve which we created ourselves: selected it, named it, demarcated it and in some cases wrote a plan for it. Time has long since soothed the physical aches and the mental frustrations, all that now remains is a pleasant sense of personal achievement, which is also a symptom of advancing age.

As District Forest Officers, each in charge of an area of between 5,000 to 10,000 square miles, most of which could be traversed only on foot, we were, had to be, strong individualists. There was little opportunity for us to get to know our fellows. More recently, the great expansion and development of forest management has necessitated much more frequent technical intercourse between officers and the District Officer is no longer completely isolated. The infrequent meetings between men with identical professional interests has often resulted in much 'shop' being talked. The reason is partly ascribed to a general sense of dedication which the average forester feels for his unusual job; it is also partly due to the continuing isolation which even today is part of the job.

The older foresters lacked the opportunity to get to know each other well and it was not until they moved up to Conservator's rank and assumed charge of several Districts, that they were able to widen and intensify their range of friends within the forestry circle. It was a rare piece of good fortune for me that, as an Assistant Conservator of Forests, I was given charge of the Learners' Training School at Sunyani at the same time that Ian Cameron was in charge of the Sunyani District. Ian is one of those gentle souls, with a great capacity for friendship which stems from a rare degree of naturalness. Few of us, alas, are true extroverts and we tend, from the unavoidable and unalterable nature of our characters, to project ourselves to the front. Individuals newly arrived at a cocktail party strike a defensive role until alcohol mellows them and flocculates them into groups. With few exceptions the theme even in the mellowed groups is personal conversational dominance. Our 'I's' project our egos.

Ian Cameron encouraged the other viewpoint; invited it and respected it, even if he disagreed with it. We had little in common save forestry. He was considerably senior to me and had served for some years in Nigeria. He spoke Hausa like a native and had married a Russian girl who like himself had leanings towards the left. Many thought Cameron a 'Bolshie', but, like many people so dubbed, he merely appeared 'Bolshie'. Ill-fortune dogged Ian's footsteps, as they often seem to do when one has no enemies. He lost one car through fire and had not insured it. Such a financial catastrophe may have been the result of bad judgement. Most of us in the days when insurance was not compulsory had no insurance. He lost another car in the Sahara and its remains still litter the sandy wastes which he twice crossed successfully.

A third car, which he had in Sunyani, was a Humber, an ex-army staff car. This gave him endless trouble and for a long time could be started only by holding together with bare hands the naked starter motor cables, a violent and painful operation with which I refused to have anything to do. It was in this car that Ian, Nina and their new-born baby, came to Sunyani. As ill-luck would have it, they were caught in a tornado, with hurricane force wind, lashing rain and violent thunder and lightning. The road from Kumasi was laterite and under such conditions could become impassable to anything but a heavy lorry, and even these were sometimes bogged down in several feet of smooth, red, oily clay.

A Cadbury and Fry cocoa lorry belting through the mud from Bechem passed the black Humber stationary on the side of the road, stopped, and discovered Ian shaking with fever, Nina semi-hysterical, and the baby howling. Leaving the palsied father, the driver crammed mother and infant in the cab of the lorry and brought them to Sunyani. I quietened Nina with half a tumbler of neat whisky and put the hungry squalling infant under a mosquito net in the bedroom while I searched for a match to light the stove to heat the baby's milk.

Staying at the resthouse was a judge of the supreme court who had drawn up that day in a vast, new, scarlet, Pontiac saloon. It was by far the most impressive car I had ever seen. My own car was an open tourer, and Littlewood, the District Commissioner had no car at all. His Honour's judicial face dropped considerably when I suggested that his was the only vehicle suitable to rescue Ian and his loads and it was with much muttering that he drove his glittering new car into the bucketing rain and through the red liquid mud towards Bechem.

The Cameron baby, named Alexander, grew strong and by 1948 was a fine lusty boy, the very apple of their eye. Tragedy then blighted their lives. Alexander's untimely death would have been tragedy enough; Fate had a more cruel blow for Ian. The ugly black Humber, intractable, uncertain and so difficult to start was the instrument. At that time new cars were rare and expensive; old ones, battered and bent by the unkind roads, were available for a song. When repairs were necessary in the bush, we usually had to do them ourselves. Only as a last resort did we call in the expert from the distant town; there lay bills which few of us cared to pay.

The black Humber, its brakes no better than the rest of it, was left in gear for safety on the drive of the Dunkwa Forestry bungalow while Ian wrestled with a part of its miserable innards. Finally to test it he switched on the ignition. Instantly the engine started of its own accord; in gear, with the car on the slightest of gradients, there was just sufficient load on the crankshaft to turn it. The engine burst into life and the car killed young Alexander who, as ill luck would have it, was behind a wheel that turned. Years later when I visited the grave-yard at Dunkwa I read the carved inscription on the head-board over the little boy's grave. With what

agony had Ian himself carved each letter of his only child's name!
Did he choose the iron-hard Odum, one of Africa's hardest woods,
deliberately? I believe so.

Not long afterwards Ian and Nina left the Coast. They bought
a cottage in the English countryside. I think he taught a little and
was not inspired. It comes to all Coasters in greater or less degree.
At twenty-five you dig up roots still only shallowly established
in English soil and transfer them to the Coast. There they ramify
in the rich warm African soil. At fifty, they are wrenched out
again. The final transplanting is often a failure. A hot-house plant
shrivels outside. Advancing age brings a coldness of itself; the old
Coaster feels trebly cold. He has no friends and that makes him
feel cold; his roots are truncated, his body chills easily; and he is
ageing.

Ian and Nina sought and found a job in the sun; in Pakistan.
They let their cottage, stored their belongings and prepared to
leave. Fate had not yet finished with them. Walking along one of
the innumerable narrow streets in Oxford, Ian was crushed against
a wall by a passing lorry. He was terribly injured and a long
incarceration in hospital seemed to have put paid to his new-found
job. The authorities were kind, however, and Fate was cheated.
Fit again, they pulled up their roots once again and transplanted
them 6,000 miles away. I hope they still flourish.

George Cansdale was one of the 'middle-distance' foresters, a
forester moreover who seemed to have more to do with animals
than trees. It is in association with animals that he will be remembered. Not many of us have his quality of quick clear thought,
untrammelled by cant, expressed succinctly. Most of us prefer the
slightly sugared approach. To the African, blunt talking is often
considered ill-mannered; the gentle, glide-path approach is not
reserved only for the diplomatist. George possessed two things that
the African liked: humour and the ability to express himself
fluently in their own language. George spoke Twi like a native and
was one of very few in the Colonial Service who achieved this
distinction, though we all had to study a language and to pass
periodic tests. It was a condition of granting an increment that
these tests were passed. Somehow we all got through them, generally without distinction, but George took the trouble, aided by an
undoubted flair for languages, to become fluent. He forsook

forestry when he was a Senior Assistant Conservator half-way up the staff list and in time almost certain to achieve the highest rank. Alas, so were several others who happened to be a little senior to him. It probably seemed to him that he was destined to continue in his present rank for many years, and that promotion when it came, would profit him little. Retirement was rigidly prescribed at fifty-five; George felt that there was too much waiting for too little. For people like Lane, Horwood, Miller and myself, all appointed together and junior to Cansdale, the road seemed even longer.

We were wrong. Only a few years later, Ghana clamoured suddenly for independence; the Convention People's Party was born and Kwame Nkrumah appeared, out of the blue, to lead it, to demand, and get, independence. In villages throughout the country south of the Volta, clenched fists were raised; the cry was 'free*dom*'; even the children cried 'dom'! For the Africans independence was the Holy Grail, its achievement a shining triumph. Freedom meant the end of Imperialism, though quite what Imperialism implied was a mystery to the mass of the people; it meant the end of exploitation; the end of the White Man. 'Go' they shouted. 'Send them home' clamoured the Press.

Forgotten was the fact that the Imperialists, whether through altruism or incidentally through greed and avarice, had lifted the people and country out of bloody barbarism and a standard of living little higher than that of the beasts of the field; had made roads, railways, installed telephones, rediffusion, equipped and staffed hospitals and provided a Government which developed industry and agriculture and had raised the standard, not to any Utopian level, but one far better than had ever been known. Fewer babies died; there was less disease; human sacrifice had almost been wiped out; travel was easy and relatively quick and the lifeblood of the country, cocoa, an industry established with the help of the Imperialists and developed to the stage where it provided more than half the world's requirements, was preserved by the farsightedness of the Government, through the Forestry Department.

What seems to have been forgotten in the hurry to sweep away the white man and decry or ignore his achievements is the fact that Imperialism was necessary. It is unthinkable that the Gold

Coast from the time when it was first colonized by the white man could have accomplished very much by itself, even if it had been left alone to fashion its own future. A score of tribes with as many languages, lacking any kind of unity, lived meagrely and uneasily in the forest zone. Disease was even more rife than murder; internecine warfare drained away the virile blood of the young men almost to the point of exhaustion. Left alone the country would be a battlefield yet.

Slavery, introduced by the Imperialists, British and others, drained away more virile blood and might ultimately have weakened the negro and retarded his progress for a millenium. The British Imperialists stopped the slave trade. They colonized the Gold Coast and the result is modern Ghana. Like Britain, Ghana has had its inescapable history of occupation; its customs have been modified, its blood improved, by invaders. The Romans and the Normans who bequeathed to the British a stamp of character, a tradition unequalled in world history, have projected this in a small measure into Ghana. Modern Ghana is what we and they, largely, have made it. What is easily forgotten, or ignored, is that if the British had not colonized Ghana, another nation would have. With what results? The answer to that question can be found in the answer to this one : 'Has any nation colonized with greater success and greater righteousness than Britain?' Look at Africa state by state and see where independence and prosperity lie. Nor should it be forgotten when the British Imperialists are castigated that the ancestors of todays Ghanaians were also colonisers, if unwilling ones, when the Mohammedans drove them from the hinterland towards the West Coast of Africa centuries ago. If there were any original inhabitants in the country now called Ghana no one knows what happened to them.

What we didn't know in 1947 was that within a decade promotion would be so rapid as to be almost farcical. The terms offered to expatriate officers who wished to leave the country, on or after independence, were fairly generous. Compensation for loss of career up to £8,000 was offered plus full pension after ten years service. Many, unwilling to reverse the roles to which they had become used i.e. to serve Africans, rather than be served by them, who feared also the unsettling events then beginning to disturb the country, the threats of violence and bloodshed, which were real, but were never properly realized, caused the cream of the Colonial Service to retire rather than join the Ghana Civil Service. We lost the Chief Conservator of Forests (F. E. Hughes), his Deputy (first Beveridge and then Harper) and seven Conservators with upwards of twenty years' service within three years, removing in one operation most of the hard core of experience. Whereas in 1938 we expected to serve at least ten years for promotion from Assistant Conservator to Senior Assistant Conservator and another five to ten years for what, for most of us was the summit, a Conservatorship, young ACF's only just confirmed were soon finding to their delight that they were Acting Conservators and soon to become substantive Conservators. I was no less fortunate: my promotion to SACF came when expected after fourteen years; within two years I was substantive Conservator; four years hence I was Deputy Chief Conservator, holding the very job which George would surely have held had he stayed on.

In the light of the known circumstances George was right to go, pensionless since he had not served his time, and take up the senior post at Regent's Park. He is a lover of animals and possesses a very close communion with them, and I think, as a firm subscriber to the view that work is a necessary evil, he was a fortunate man to be able to do what he liked and to be paid well for it. How right he was became evident when he made his name on television and his *Looking at Animals* series achieved high popularity and made him a well-known personality. Maybe he was too successful?

My wife and I were paying our regular leave visit to the London Zoo in 1952 hoping to see George, as well as his charges. We asked for him at the reception desk, to be informed that he was attending an important meeting. How important that meeting was was indicated by the positive galaxy of gleaming Rolls Royces which we had observed parked outside. It was this meeting, beyond the door of which we stood for a moment, that was removing him from the service of the Zoological Society. When we got back to Town hours later he was front-page news in all the evening papers.

In George we lost a good man, and periodically he informs me of his regrets at leaving West Africa. He followed his star, which is what we all do, consciously or unconsciously, for better or worse. In his case it was, for some time at least, very much better.

Above: The British Prime Minister in a 'Mammy' chair, Ghana 1960.
Below: Surf boats plying off Accra.

MAIN ROAD ACCRA

Above: Old Accra, 1916. *Below:* Accra today.

Because of independence and a desire not to be dependent upon a raw, untrained bureaucracy, the very flower of the Department chose compensation and early retirement. None of us is indispensable and no one can say that the Department's progress after the self-removal of the core of experience has been better or worse. At the time when Conservator after Conservator shook the red dust of Ghana from his feet for the last time, it seemed catastrophic; and it appeared likely that the younger and relatively untried remaining expatriates would delay progress and expansion by reason of their inexperience. The cataclysm never occurred, or if it did it was not evident to the survivors!

Dr Charles Taylor, ascetically inclined, an inveterate gossip, had been Silviculturist in the vital post-war years, and his quick and ready reason, and the rare attention he gave to detail so essential in the research worker, was a main plank in our planning. Many of us thought it difficult to find a more suitable successor than Alastair Douglas who had acted in the post on several occasions and was regarded generally as an automatic choice when Charles went. The Chief Conservator thought differently, however, and selected Donald Lane. Douglas joined the long queue of retirers and Donald remained in Kumasi as Silviculturist and captain of the golf club.

Mike Harley had just relinquished his post as Working Plans officer. This tall, lively Scot with considerable humour lacing his often sharp tongue, was the right man for this demanding, expanding, vital job. When Chidlow Vigne was Acting Chief Conservator and disliking the job intensely as a good research man will dislike administration, I recall his observation that if he *had* to do the job he would choose Mike as his Deputy. I can think of no higher tribute to Mike's abilities. Mike in turn relieved David Kinloch, who went to lecture students at my old University at Bangor on forestry. David is that rare individual, the natural teacher. His slow easy charm, complete self effacement, encyclopaedic knowledge—and the patience and facility to impart that knowledge—will be an asset to any teaching faculty.

The obvious choice of Working Plans officer to replace Mike Harley was John Mooney. Mooney must have put up more backs than any other individual I have ever known, and in less time. His impact on forestry, straight from the cockpit of a Fleet Air Arm fighter, was akin to a tornado on the high forest; we were left shaken and bruised. His tongue is a whiplash by its forthrightness and the fact that he is so often right does not increase his popularity. This is a pity for I consider him to be a scrupulously honest and fair person, possessed of a shrewd brain, a quick wit and tremendous enthusiasm. Mentally I would rate his capacity higher than any member of the Department I have known. Perhaps being an only child has made him intolerant and blunt sometimes to the point of rudeness, without meaning to be rude. Nothing can eschew his academic soundness, however, or deny his considerable charm.

My first contact with this young man was in his first tour. I came upon a four-page, closely typed letter addressed by him to Beveridge, Conservator of Forests, Ashanti, which I read to the end with growing amazement. It was a violent criticism of the Bobiri Working Plan, the brain child of David Kinloch and Alistair Foggie, two of the most capable and painstaking management experts we had. It says as much for Mooney's abilities as for the forbearance of the Chief Conservator (Alistair Foggie) that he was promoted, on merit, from Assistant Conservator to Conservator within the short space of eight years.

John is now Silviculturist after a successful and wearying tour as Working Plans officer, and I prophesy that he will achieve more silvicultural progress than any of his predecessors.

Tall, blond Dennistoun Duff joined the general exodus partly, I think, because he could not see the African in his present stage of emancipation as competent to direct his own affairs. There were too many 'bushmen' and he was not prepared to be an executive to hair-brained corrupt politicians who sought only the political kingdom. Duff was scrupulously fair to the competent African but suffered the incompetents with less gladness even than John Mooney.

From the beginning, I had intended to leave the service while I was still young enough and fit enough to pioneer a new career. I had not fixed a date, but I reckoned that at forty-five, after twenty years, I should have completed my stint. I almost left five years earlier when I was informed that I was to be posted to Accra as Headquarters Assistant, a dogsbody's job which faced everyone who hoped to mount the promotion ladder. For my wife's sake I was not averse to a tour in Accra in spite of the considerable financial loss this would entail. I was then running both the Dunkwa and Wiawso Districts in the Western Region and though conducive to stomach ulcers, the vast amount of car travel involved earned me travelling allowances in the £1,000 a year class. I was not silly enough to boast of this, or to claim that I lived on my car and travelling allowances as one misguided Agricultural Survey Officer did, and thereby secured himself an 'armchair' job for the rest of his career. Allowances were by no means all profit; I wore out two motor cars on the cart tracks they called roads in that area; tyres lasted no time at all and exhaust pipes fell off with sickening regularity. I declined the 'offer' however when I learnt that my family and I would have to live in the Club Resthouse in Accra because of the shortage of accommodation in the capital. In a letter to Hughes, the Chief Conservator, I said that if this transfer were imposed on me I should hand in my papers. A year earlier I could not have afforded to do this as I should have lost my pension, as did George Cansdale. The resurgence of Ghana, however, offered accelerated promotion to many of us and saved me from what must have been a purgatorial tour.

The modern bungalows built for civil servants in Ghana are little more than contemporary boxes. In the bush stations, however, bungalows in the early days were built to give the occupier a sense of freedom and to keep out as much heat as possible. Rooms were usually large, and high-ceilinged, and there were plenty of them. Verandahs to keep out the sun were long and wide. The club resthouses were temporary quarters erected during the war (some might asked pointedly 'which war?') and have been maintained on a temporary basis ever since. Some officers have been obliged to *live* there, for the great expansion of Government Service saw no equivalent expansion in quarters which Government are obliged to provide for its expatriates. They were, and still are, dirty, dismal, degrading and badly furnished. Their only advantages are that they are within a stone's throw of the sea and are next door to the Accra Club, whence good meals can always be obtained. Today, officers refuse to stay there if they can get accommodation elsewhere even at their own expense. On the few occasions we stayed there no alternative accommodation was available. So primitive were the arrangements, and still are, that

although electric light was available, I had to climb on top of a
wardrobe to plug our electric kettle into the light socket to heat
water for the baby's feed. After it had boiled I had to climb up
again to bring the kettle down. As this had to be done every three
hours it was a somewhat hazardous procedure especially as the
three of us occupied one small room. There were no fans and no
water sanitation. One night stands out as *the ultimate* in discomfort and frustration. Never, before, or since, has either of us
endured such purgatory. Three nights I once spent sleeping on a
wooden bench in the third-class waiting room in Strasbourg railway station in 1937 were dreamland by comparison.

It was a Saturday night during the hot season and the brisk
breeze which comes off the sea all day had died as it always does
at night. Windows are few and doors must be shut in Accra, where
thieves are more plentiful and bolder than elsewhere. More than
one young officer has lost his trousers and their contents and one
lost his watch and wallet from beneath his pillow, a loss he did
not discover till morning. We sweated beneath the stuffy mosquito net, praying for coolness and sleep. The baby, teething,
alternately whimpered and howled. At 10 pm loud music started
up at the Club. Saturday night, I remembered, was dance night.
At 11 pm more music began, with amplifiers so efficient that
from the King George V Memorial Hall whence this music
emanated, we could hear the sharp intake of breath as the MC
announced each dance. From that time till 3 am the bands
(one 'potted', one live) vied with each other. Occasionally we heard
one, solo, but usually they played against each other, melody,
tempo and mood, all in endless cacophanous conflict.

At 3 am the Club band ceased. At 4 am King George V
went home. At last we thought, sleep would come. It was cooler
now and a faint stirring of breeze from the land made itself felt.
We slept, even the baby. We slept for a few minutes till the loud
close bleat of a goat and sounds of human voices from the cell
next door awoke us. It was a middle-aged couple who years before
had been kind to me in Sunyani. They were quarrelling and their
pet goat was bleating. After kicking the goat out of the way and
chasing it into the night, and begging our neighbours to allow us
to sleep, we again lay down. I was about to fall into the deep abyss
of oblivion when steel-tipped heels began to hammer a sharp

rhythmic tattoo on the cement floored corridor which ran the the whole 100-yard length of the resthouse. The late reveller, whistling between his teeth, marched merrily past our door and the sound of his heel tips gradually receded, then stopped at the latrine. Tensed, I debated which way he would turn when he came out. *Away* to the right, or *back* the way he had come? I visualized this man, monkey-jacketed, pleasantly weary after an enjoyable night's dancing and drinking, looking forward to a long morning's slumber undisturbed by babies, bands, goats, or quarrelling couples, undressing and climbing into his lone bed, and sleeping! The door of the latrine slammed and heel tips sounded their sharp infuriating tattoo past our door, receding gradually into the distance. Bette and I groaned simultaneously and slept as dawn broke.

My appointment as Headquarters Assistant was not pressed and shortly afterwards following the proposed retirement of Taylor and Kinloch I suddenly found myself 'Acting Conservator i/c Ashanti'. I relieved Duff who went to Western Region and was shortly to retire. The Conservator's office in Kumasi, capital of Ashanti, was formerly one of the bedrooms of the old resthouse, and one in which I had slept a few days after my first arrival in Ghana. My desk was where the bed had stood seventeen years before; the latrine just outside had the same thunderbox and the same crooked three-inch nail protruding from the wall. My wheel had turned full circle.

A curious coincidence occurred during my very first day in the office. I was feeling the heady elation which all of us must experience on the first attainment of high office. Although I was only Acting, I knew that barring accidents I should be substantive Conservator within a year. My charge now embraced the four Districts in which I had served as a junior ACF—Juaso, where I had first relieved Cansdale, Sunyani, where I had got to know Ian Cameron, Bekwai, which I had never liked, and Kumasi, which I had only recently taken over from Coldwells. I felt pleased with myself and did not allow the fact that fortune had smiled on me to cloud my elation.

I walked slowly around the large office—my former bedroom—glanced at the wall maps showing all the Ashanti Reserves, some of which I had created, the list of concessions, the calendar of returns, the big mahogany map-chests—and out on to the wooden verandah looking west towards the post-office and over the drive-in. Parked below me was a car I well knew, a pale blue ('moonstone grey' I recall from the brochure) eight-cylinder Ford saloon. I had bought it in 1947, my first new car. I had sold it, regretfully, after a year, for I had been sent to do a year's post graduate course at the Imperial Forestry Institute and I could not afford to take it with me.

A little later that morning who should walk into my office but Wenman to whom I had sold the car. We talked business, and then, assuming that the car was still his, I enquired how it was running. He astonished me by saying that he had sold the car months ago and had not seen it since. I thought what a startling coincidence it was that he and the car should turn up independently within a few minutes of each other.

Assistant Conservators of Forests of strong character such as 'Helen' Wills and Mike Horwood used to take no liquor with them when they went to bush. As most of their time was spent in bush, their drinking time was short, highly concentrated and sometimes disastrous. Some even stronger characters such as Cansdale and Taylor eschewed drink and tobacco entirely. I must confess that I needed an alcoholic stimulant when I lived in the bush and regarded it as no great hardship to forgo alcohol in station.

The effect of bush life on men like Wills, Horwood, Cansdale and Taylor, evidently was not the same as on lesser mortals such as myself. They completed their day's trekking and were content to spend an evening in their tents with a pint of squash and an old newspaper or book. By the time I had got through the day and sat sweating in my camp chair, I felt I had earned a drink, needed one, and jolly well had one. But then I have never liked the forest. Addiction to drink is not uncommon among Forest Rangers; neither is it particularly common, which is a tribute to the stern stuff of which they are made. Many of them are teetotallers and non-smokers. I cannot say the same of Forest Guards, though the incidence of topers among them is not as high as the rough, lonely life they lead might warrant.

That one can be bush-happy, I have no doubt and the sensitive soul, the less well-balanced personality, cannot tolerate considerable loneliness without some slight mental disturbance. It may not be an obvious disturbance, it often is not evident in the man's work or behaviour. He might 'hit the bottle' in his spare time and so gradually destroy himself.

That there have not been more tragedies like that of F. K. Chey is a tribute to the resilience of the human body. Chey was clever and given proper guidance and the sort of chance that I had, might have been brilliant. He was the outstanding pupil in the first Learners School I taught in 1940. A short slim young man with an open alert face, voluble tongue and enquiring mind, he was also likeable. He was a pleasure to teach because he learned so readily and cheerfully. He pleased the eye also because of the care he took with his clothes and the attention he gave to his grooming.

In 1956, Chey came into my office in Kumasi wishing to see me. At that moment I was in earnest discussion with John Mooney. I thought it odd that Chey should rudely interrupt our conversation. I had not seen him for years, but all I could do at that moment was to ask him to wait a little, and reflect briefly that I had never known him to be rude before. A few minutes later he again interrupted us at a point in the discussion where I needed all my faculties to understand the point John was making. I was a little angry and said rather curtly that he must wait until I had finished. He turned to go without a word and I was struck by the emptiness of his expression, it was vacant like a fetish priest's face in a trance as though he had passed beyond despair to the last gate in the road and found it locked. But I was too preoccupied to ponder this. I never saw him again. He was killed a few minutes later.

Francis Kwadjo Chey's Forestry career spanned eleven years and was not attended by the success I had hoped and of which I knew him capable. He worked under me when I was in charge of the Sunyani Forest District in 1940 and 1943. He and I surveyed the boundaries of the proposed Sawsaw Reserve through which the Sunyani-Wenchi road runs and near where my car caught fire. The period of the survey was characterized by almost incessant rain and as we crawled around mile after mile of inundated boundary line, the prismatic compass had periodically to be stripped and emptied of water. For nearly two weeks I carried my ·22 rifle hoping at least to have occasional pigeon pie. Only on the last day, when I left the weapon in the tent, did I see anything shootable. As recounted in *The Perpetual Forest*, on that last day I encountered a veritable menagerie of beasts.

Chey seemed normal to me; he was married with a baby son and appeared happy. He always worked with zest; he was an excellent Ranger and his reports bore the stamp of considerable pains taken. Many Rangers' reports give the impression of having been written on a boundary line, in the rain, using a cement pillar as a table.

When I took over the School again in 1946, I maintained contact with Chey as I did with all the Learner Rangers who had the misfortune to receive my tuition. Of all those I taught, only two let me, and themselves down. They told me he was drinking and that his work was shoddy, which astonished me. I last spoke kindly to him when he visited me in 1946. He then looked an unhappy man, yet he would reveal no clue as to the cause of this unhappiness. He admitted that he sometimes drank more than he should, but I doubted if alcohol was the main reason why he looked and behaved like a hopeless soul. He seemed to have plumbed unknown depths of despair for other secret reasons. Years later I was told of his dismissal for general inefficiency.

I would dearly have liked to talk with him that day in Kumasi, and perhaps I should have dismissed John Mooney and done so. Perhaps, if I had, Chey would still be alive, though whether he would particularly wish to be alive is another matter. A log from a moving timber lorry fell on him and crushed him to pulp. I am not unduly introspective, John Ramsay says I have no imagination whatever, and am no believer in fate. At the same time I have a slightly uneasy feeling that fate and Chey and I were somehow involved. If so, the purpose is beyond me.

CHAPTER THREE

The Training of a Forester

FOR the great majority of men, the choice of a career is a gamble. It is difficult enough to choose a wife with whom to live amicably for fifty years but at least one has the opportunity to get to know something of one's future wife. Most marriages which survive do so by the earnest application of each partner to the difficult problem of living together. The majority of marriages are a success only because we make them so. Much the same can be said of most careers. Those of us, surely in the great minority, who, when obliged to make our choice of life's work have done so certainly and cheerfully, are lucky. Few of us know what we want and fewer still in our 'teens.

In the days when Man was, by force, a hunter, he had no choice but to hunt and his sons became hunters as soon as they could wield a club. Life was considerably simpler: a man might have to ' work ' to get his wife a fur or to bring home meat, tasks which might be completed in one fell swoop, but having pleased his wife and filled the larder for a week, or a month, depending on the weather, he was free to amuse himself. In what way is not clear. The tobbaco habit had not been discovered; nor had the football pool, the ' pub ' or the ' telly '. Life was probably rough, short perhaps, but uncomplicated.

Today, a cycle of worry begins its endless movement with the parents. Before children reach the age of worry, parents begin to ponder their futures. Schools and careers are important; by the time the offspring have reached the difficult adolescent years the parents may be approaching their dotage! By the time children have decided what they are going to be, and have become what they want to be, they themselves are near the stage of marriage, and so the cycle continues.

I did not know what I wanted to be until it was too late to be it! I was a Bachelor of Science in Natural History before I made my

c*

first choice of career; fortunately no one wanted a plant pathologist and I am very glad now that they did not, I should have dis-
liked the job, I now know. At the age of twenty I was in love with
a title: Plant Pathologist! Now it makes me shudder. As a small
boy I was, in some ways, as shy as a girl. In that I was probably
unfortunate. As a small boy I was made into a journalist. In that I
was fortunate, though I believed myself ill-used.

My father, having been a coal miner and then a newspaper boy,
became a journalist and by his own efforts made himself a
great journalist and a competent writer. He was driven as a small
boy drives the pedals of his tricycle, by a furious urge to get somewhere, to succeed. He did not reach great eminence: he was too
furious in his arguments. But he knew what he wanted and he got
it. Everything he did was at top speed; accurate to a letter, but
speedy. I can still hear the heels of his boots driving him along at
top speed; the sound of his typewriter went on and on into the
night, at top speed. He must have been one of the very few people
in the world who could write shorthand at 230 words a minute,
and read them back, and produce a certificate to prove it. He was
that kind of man.

Journalism both attracted and terrified me. I was thrust into it
in my early 'teens during school holidays and given small jobs to
do which I hated. Being shy with people I particularly dreaded
the interviews I was asked to make by a father anxious that I
should be competent at something. My school reports were, at this
stage, such that I once made alterations to the final marks, so that
the weight of my father's criticism might be lightened somewhat.
My deceit was insufficiently thorough, however, and when he
totalled up the individual subject marks and discovered the total
to be considerably less than the amended total, being nothing if
not thorough, he promptly penned a note to the headmaster.
J. M. Judd, MA (Cantab) was a tall lean forbidding man who wore
pince nez and yellow boots. He terrified me and I had not forgotten
the last flogging he had administered to me. He had hurt me,
though I hadn't cried. I felt like crying, however, as my father
sealed the envelope containing his note and handed it to me for
delivery. I had no need of my imagination to conjure up a vision
of the shape of things to come. I did the only possible thing. I
'lost' the note and said nothing about it. To my inexpressible

relief my father appeared to forget about it and I did no more juggling with school reports. It was understandable that my father should at least try and ensure that I knew the elements of writing good English. At the age of twelve, through his good offices, I was a week-end sports reporter and for the sum of 2s 6d, paid weekly, by the *South Wales Football Echo*, I gathered as many football and hockey results as I could and telephoned them to the *Echo* every Saturday evening during the season.

When it rained, as it often did, I got as wet as the players and seemed to suffer a perpetual cold. But 2s 6d a week was a lot of money for a twelve-year old in those days. For 7s 6d, I recall, I bought myself a gleaming acetylene lamp for my bicycle which some fool blew up by sticking a match in the gas generating chamber, while I was in the saddle. We never found all the bits.

Occasionally I was sent to a Trade Union Congress meeting, my father being a staunch union man who liked long verbatim reports of such meetings which my inadequate shorthand rarely supplied. Occasionally, armed with a press pass, I browsed around agricultural shows and can still recall more than one free lunch as a 'press man'. As I grew older and less shy, I found myself writing a few paragraphs lifted from the local 'rags', as my father called them, for the morning edition of the *Daily Herald*, which he had now joined as its South Wales representative, leaving with relief the Conservative *Western Mail*. News that broke during the day appeared in its sister 'rag' the *South Wales Echo* and it was not considered unethical to 'lift' this, re-write it and telephone it through to London by private wire to appear in the following day's *Herald*. I was given some exciting and many more boring jobs to do. One of the latter was to rise with the dawn and cycle from our house in Rhiwbina, four miles to Cardiff to do a 'fudge'. The London papers reached Cardiff on the newspaper train very early in the morning. They were then distributed to the shops and newspaper sellers all over the area. This was a rushed routine job which never concerned me. As the *Herald* went to bed about midnight news of importance which broke between then and the time of distribution, shortly after dawn, could only be added by the use of a Stop Press. On such occasions, as for example when there was a world championship boxing match in America, arrangements would be made beforehand for the early edition of the *Herald*, many thousand copies, to be run through a cyclostyling machine where it would have the result imprinted in the Stop Press column. My job was to condense the news item into a few words, type these on a wax in such a form that they would fit neatly into the Stop Press column. I then handed the wax to the distribution manager and cycled home to breakfast. At 10s a time I suppose I was overpaid.

One day I was handed a cheque for £5,000 and told to deliver it to the winner of the *Herald* cross-word puzzle. The paper's Rolls Royce was put at my disposal and, in torrential rain, I drove, of all places, to the village of Ystradgynlais, my birth place, some fifty miles away west of Swansea, to present this cheque to an unemployed miner with a wife and seven children. The miner and his family lived in a tenement designed for two adults. His £5,000 winnings could have bought up the whole miserable block. I often wonder what he did with this small fortune and whether he invested it, as he declared he would, for the education of his children.

I made a mild scoop out of a coroner's inquest on a murdered man, a crime which I believe is still unsolved. 'The mystery of the red-headed woman' headlined in the *Herald* was exclusive, and a solution of that mystery might have led to the murderer's arrest. At that stage I left school with no idea of what I wanted to do in life. I had a firm step on the ladder of journalism, thanks to my father's insistence, and although I enjoyed writing I had nothing to write about (many rejection slips emphasized this fact) and I felt no enthusiasm about collecting news. This, perhaps, was laziness: I dreamed of writing with no ties. Thirty years later I have the same dream!

Academically I was outstanding at nothing: I was a good woodworker and wrote a fair composition; the rest was indifferent to poor not withstanding prodigious effort. I had no enthusiasms. Many young men at seventeen must find themselves in this position. At seventeen, after two years in the fifth form, I matriculated, much to the astonishment of my masters and my own delight.

I was fortunate in my parents, both of solid north-country stock, though my father's sense of urgency and the aim of perfection which he set for me caused no end of friction and upsets throughout my school career and afterwards. He expected perfection and I never attained it. Because of this we rarely saw eye-to-eye and were never companions. In his sense of duty to his children, however, he could not be faulted. He was not a rich man and was still fighting his furious way to the top of the journalistic ladder when he offered me the choice of newspaper work or University. If the latter, he was anxious that I should become a doctor. This was one career I *knew* I could not follow.

I chose the University, without any idea what it portended, or what I wanted to study. Other schoolboys I knew had positive aims; they knew, or seemed to know, what they wanted out of life. I had no idea. Louis Thomas, later to die tragically and for no apparent good reason, was a friend of my father and Registrar of the local University College of South Wales and Monmouthshire at Cardiff. I went to see him at my father's behest.

His first question was 'What are you good at?'. I replied I was good at nothing but not bad at Chemistry. To which he made a remark which, in view of what was to happen in the field of chemistry during the next thirty years, betrayed an astonishing ignorance of the trend of events. 'There is no future in Chemistry,' he declared. Finally, 'What about biology?' This it seemed offered a field of enormous scope. In view of what was to happen to me, he was wrong again.

Biology, I knew, meant animals and plants. It had not been on my school's curriculum, much to my later sorrow, and I had only the vaguest notion of what its study implied. It sounded interesting and easy. Rather like a customer in a shop, uncertain of what he wants, I was 'sold' biology. It was nevertheless a happy choice, for although I have always been a poor academist, lacking the logic and patience which is necessary in science; while I later forsook biology as a career, the study of living things continues to fascinate me and helped me to achieve, in a small measure, my ambition to write, which means to write for profit.

I enrolled as a student, an undergraduate, my subjects being Botany, Zoology and Chemistry, with Physics as a subsidiary. I proved then and have maintained since, that anyone who is not subnormal, provided he is willing to work hard enough, can take a degree in Natural History. He, or she, can acquire by the same token, a good honours degree. He is unlikely to get a First, any more than I did, coming an expected cropper in some of the practical subjects. I gambled on a First in Botany and lost. To have studied the whole curriculum during my degree course probably would not have failed me in the degree examinations; but I could afford to take no chances and ignored almost completely the systematic side. I did not feel I had the time to study classification properly, and I certainly begrudged the effort. As a result some of my identifications were oddly at variance with reality, even though I took into the laboratory an illustrated flora quite without realizing the fact and without taking advantage of it. For the 'prac' we were allowed a flora and this was supposed to be inspected at the door by Parsons the laboratory attendant. Perhaps old Parsons took me for an honest man, at any rate he did not bother even to open the flora which if he had would have revealed to him at once a wealth of illustrations which would have failed me had it been discovered lying unopened as it was on the bench beside me.

The Honours Course was a different kettle of fish. 'Prac' took not a couple of hours but two whole days. No floras were allowed and the flowering plants we were asked to identify were all exotic. We had to know the families. Guesses were futile and I attempted none. However good the rest of the 'prac' may have been, however erudite my theory, I knew then that I was not going to get a First. I got a 2A, the next best thing; but getting a Second, even at the A level, is like playing in the Second XV; you never shout about it.

Frankly I was not worth a First. Neither apparently were the others. 'Dai' Davies might have got his 2B because he sliced off the top of his cutting thumb. For making thin sections of plant material for microscopic examination we used flat-bladed razors; his slipped and there was blood everywhere and no chance of his being able to cut a section let alone identify it. I was able without much risk to slip him a piece of blotting paper with the identification he was seeking scrawled on it.

'Bessie' Higgs on the same bench as me, could probably have got me a First. She knew I had no hope with the flowers whereas she was good at that sort of thing, but no enlightening slip of blotting paper came my way. Miss Higgs got a 2B. Kate Williams, who would have helped me if she could, got a Third.

The year was 1934. There I was a B.Sc. (Hons). I thought myself no end of a lad. No one else seemed to think any differently about me, however, except Father who was disappointed that I had not got a First. 1934 was not a good year for graduates. I console myself with that fact. Unlike the others of my year I was not to become a teacher. That at least I did know. I wanted, I thought, to be a plant pathologist and much of my recent energy had been directed into that channel. My special subject (we all had one) was 'The study of a pathogen infecting the roots of cucumber'. As a result of much overtime I finally discovered the fungus responsible and added my name to botanical history. *Olpidium major* Sp. Nov. Cook and Collins. I discovered it; Cook, the senior Botany lecturer, confirmed it and captured half the glory. I wrote the pamphlet which was published under our joint names; I even did the drawing for the end plate. I had not the sense to inscribe my name or initials on it so that few believed me when I said the work was mine, the writing was mine, and the drawings too. I thought then, and still think, that Dr Cook, whose name appeared regularly in the world's scientific press, might have given me a moment of glory. In pure science, no less than on the stage, publicity is a vital rung in the ladder of success.

In 1934 there were few jobs going. It was during the slump and no one wanted an inexperienced B.Sc. with a leaning towards fungi and plant pathology. My only chance, said Professor McLean, was to do some research, gain experience and aim for a M.Sc. The equivalent degree of M.A. comes automatically to graduates at Oxford and Cambridge but in most provincial Universities one must *earn* a Master's degree. Usually two year's research work is needed before one can present an original thesis which will satisfy the examiners.

I believe I was mentally lazy and illogical, two failings which no research worker can profitably suffer. But my chief fault is probably a stubbornness born of north country breeding. In spite of Dr Cook's sensible advice that because there were no facilities for the study of plant pathology at Cardiff I should concentrate on the more straightforward mycological research, I insisted on the former, with its quite complex problems of cause and effect. Mycology is mainly cause, a study of the organism itself rather than its effect. As a result I began a study of *Septoriosis in Chrysanthemums*. It was never finished. After a year, I gave up, seeing no end to the problem, held up by a lack of co-operation between an Italian pathologist at the instigation of Mussolini's Govern-

ment, as a mild reprisal for the British Government's imposition
of sanctions against Italy during the Ethiopian crisis. At that
point I would have become a journalist like a shot. But no one
wanted me!

I began to write about the things which interested me most,
animals. Three years of Zoology had taught me a lot and much
of what I wrote was immature and plagiaristic. Most of it was
thrown back at me with neat depressing rejection slips attached.
I was in the doldrums. All my school friends were by now firmly
established in jobs; my University contemporaries were either
teaching or had completed their Masters' theses. I felt very sorry
for myself.

Then, in 1936, a friend of my father, Sir Richard Llewellyn, a
landowner in West Wales, brought to my attention vacancies for
Forest Officers in the Colonies. Why not try for one? It would
mean taking a degree in Forestry, another two years of study, but
the reasonable certainty of a job abroad.

My people were willing to send me to Oxford. They were probably more upset by my unemployment than I, and were anxious,
as always, to do all they could. As my brother John was a boarder
at Cowbridge Grammar School and nearing University age, their
financial burden would be considerably increased if I went away.
Bangor, which had a Forestry school was cheaper by far and,
though the glamour of an Oxford degree attracted me, I considered myself enough of a burden and chose the cheaper University College. It may be that an Oxford degree commands greater
respect than any other and has a slightly greater pull initially.
There is little doubt that all other things being equal an employer
prefers a man with an Oxford degree rather than one from a provincial University. This preference is much less marked than it
used to be. Thereafter, it matters not: ability, application and
luck, are the important things.

Whether an Oxford Forestry degree is *better* than that of a
provincial University I very much doubt. Having studied at both
Bangor and Oxford, I would say not. There is more physiological
division of labour at Oxford: more people trying to teach you the
same things; more facilities and the tutor system, which ought to
add up to an advantage over the less affluent, and smaller, University Colleges. The end-product is much the same, and though the

Oxford man may be the more poised and self-assured, the provincial man soon gets the corners rounded off once on the job.

With the benefits of a Natural History degree and a few years of experience, I found life at Bangor pleasantly easy. I played as much rugby football and cricket as I could and there were few afternoons in winter or summer when I was not playing with a ball. With Snowdon in sight (my 'digs' were in Snowdon View) winter and spring were inclined to be wet and as the rugby field was sited on the highest point in Bangor, overlooking the island of Anglesey and the narrow Menai Straits, we became inured to both mud and rain. When I wasn't playing games, reading lecture notes or attending field excursions, which play so large a part in the teaching of a practical subject such as Forestry, I wrote. I earned little, but still I wrote and I have scarcely stopped since. Once a year came Rag Week, a time of hair loosening at all 'red brick' Universities and in my last academic year, I was proud to be given the Editorship of the Rag Newspaper *The Tonicle*.

The Forestry degree examinations went off with only a single incident as far as I was concerned. On the Saturday the cricket XI travelled to Manchester to play the University, whom we narrowly defeated. We made the most of our time in Manchester and did not entrain for Bangor till Sunday, arriving late that night suffering from a lack of sleep and a surfeit of English beer. On the Monday at 9 am I was due to attend my final *viva voce* before Professor H. M. Steven, the external examiner. At 9 am I was rudely awakened by my co-digger 'Del' Owen (now a Forestry lecturer at Bangor) and informed that the Professor awaited me. Unshaven, in dressing-gown and slippers, I ran the quarter-mile from the digs, all down hill I am glad to say, into the Forestry building and espying the door of the Professor's room open, entered at speed.

I weighed a little under thirteen stone at the time and most of it met Prof. Steven as he was about to leave the room. An irresistible force encountering a movable object, as it were. He went over like a skittle pin while I stood there shaking with trepidation and exertion, mumbling apologies.

The *viva* was perhaps more searching than if I had presented myself on time, properly dressed, shaven and lacking that effluvium which advertises a beery 'morning after'. All I can recall of that *viva* was being accused of being a Lamarckian and in attempting to explain that I was not, getting myself inextricably entangled in an argument which I lost hands down. Notwithstanding, I passed and obtained a satisfactory report.

I was a qualified forester and had, I hoped, completed my academic training. It had lasted eight years. Many of my friends who had left school at the same time as myself were successful businessmen, some with wives and children. I had still to find a job. My first job was a temporary one as a surveyor for the Forestry Commission. I had applied for several professional appointments, one with the Commission, to whom I had admitted at the interview that I had also applied for a Colonial Service appointment and would prefer such an appointment. This admission, I thought, would probably exclude me from their consideration, but as I was to discover twenty years later, when I myself sat on selection boards, honesty is the best policy in such matters. I was stationed in mid-Wales at the village of Llanidloes, which was a day's travel from Cardiff, though as the crow flies the distance is about 100 miles. The village lies near the foot of Plynlimmon, from whose flanks the embryo River Severn emerges. My job took me daily near the mountain top, a place of wild winds, heather and bog. My instructions were to survey and mark with white posts the compartment boundaries of a forest, as yet unborn. The area, which excluded the mountain summit above the tree limit, was roughly marked on the field sheets, which were characterized by vast expanses of blank paper, rather like the empty spaces on the Ghana maps showing the uninhabited areas which I was later to traverse.

The Commission paid me £2 10s a week; it wasn't much, but it was my first job and I was happy. It was to give me a foretaste, had I but known it, of the loneliness which was to afflict me like a disease in Ghana. During the weeks in which I strode the high steep flanks of Plynlimmon, I saw no one. Cadman, the District Officer, came once to view the land and having done so departed hastily never to return in my time. The only constantly visible living creatures were the buzzards, which I tried in vain to photograph at close range, wheeling high in the blue sky, calling their repetitive thin cries; below me a few ponies and sheep nibbled at the unappetizing pasture. The Romans are said once to have dug lead in this area and the evidence of this was numbers of deep holes fenced to keep out straying ponies, sheep, and wandering surveyors.

I wore a waterproof zip jacket, shorts and high rubber boots and what with the steep slopes, and the four-feet long posts I had to lug around to plant at all changes of direction, I was a fit man by the time I handed in my field books and maps, no longer empty but compartmented and measured.

My temporary job was twice interrupted; once to take advantage of a small bursary I had won to attend the British Association's meeting at Cambridge, and once to attend the interview at the Colonial Office. There, a number of us (one of whom borrowed and never returned a very fine knife I had, complete with scissors and a gadget for getting stones out of horse's hooves) were interviewed by a board comprising some very imposing senior Forest Officers who gave us a fair grilling designed not to ascertain whether we had played in the first XV but whether we knew anything about the jobs for which we had applied. It was afterwards that another gentleman enquired about our social and athletic prowess. After the interview I returned to Llanidloes and continued to clamber about the mountain. I caught my first and only trout, and what I thought at the time was the biggest fresh-water monster ever to be hooked. I crossed the Severn daily, usually with a light-hearted and not very long jump, for it was near its source and rarely more than a few feet across. Here and there were some wide and deep pools occasionally with miniature waterfalls cascading merrily into them. After the mountain of loneliness it was a joy to sit on the bank and listen to the water's talking. I carried a cheap trout rod in my rucksack and if I wasn't too tired on my long journey home—I had five miles of rough road to cycle after the scramble down the mountain and my working day was rarely less than twelve hours—I would bait a worm and angle, dozing in the afternoon warmth, lulled by the voice of the embryo river. Periodically I wound up the hook and re-baited it. I was, and am, no fisherman and angled solely for the pot. On this sunny afternoon I reeled in to experience a 'bite' that nearly pulled the rod from my hands. I let the line run a bit, then, drowsy no longer, began to play this monster fish. For ten minutes or so I reeled in and out as the beast at the other end appeared to go and come. Then, tired of the play, I decided come what may, to have done and wound the reel till the rod bent and threatened to break. With my back against the heather-clad bank and my heels dug well in I persevered till I had hauled into view what seemed to be an endless length of galvanized steel wire. That ended my day's fishing.

My 'digs' were with the local butcher, a small, thin man who seemed to spend most of his time in the local pub. His wife, his very antithesis in size and habits, fed me royally on the best of the meat in the shop. I ate like a horse and slept like a log. Then one Sunday morning, as I was filling in the final details of the survey on the less barren looking field-sheets, my temporary job suddenly ended. A telegram from my home said simply 'Telephone me—Mother'. I went out to the local telephone box and put through a call. It was good news. I had been selected, subject to medical fitness, as Assistant Conservator of Forests, Nigeria.

That evening I regaled the butcher's family with bottled cider. 'Mrs Butcher' sipped a wineglassful 'just to celebrate' but the butcher and I drank deeply that night. The following Monday it blew hard on Plynlimmon and with it came rain. I got wet and cold, and pedalled painfully back to my 'digs' with what appeared to be a knife through my right kidney and little hope of medical fitness at the forthcoming medical examination. With the aid of hot compresses and lavish application of liniment, most of the pain had disappeared by the time I took train to Liverpool, thinking gloomily of diseased kidneys and visions of awful medical failure.

Dr Le Fanu's surgery was on the first floor of a large house, overlooking one of the main thoroughfares of Liverpool via a large dormer window. Passers-by must have seen some queer sights through the thinly curtained glass, including large naked young men leaping about, if my performance was a standard one. The doctor gave me a thorough examination and when I had completed a violent hopping exercise on alternate legs, had blood pressure and eyes tested, and my external orifices probed, I was told to dress and produce a 'specimen'. I could not do so. In my own mind this had some connection with diseased kidneys, revealing a sad lack of knowledge of human physiology. I kept the doctor waiting for some minutes before returning to him with empty container and an agonizing confession of failure. He seemed in no way perturbed. 'Take the glass upstairs,' he said, 'and pull the lavatory chain.' The lavatory water gushed and so did I. Dr Le Fanu's parting words were encouraging, 'Drink moderately and keep away from the women,' he advised as he pocketed my one-and-a-half guineas.

It was two weeks before my appointment was confirmed. During that time I resigned my temporary job, returned home and began a study of Nigeria. Then, for reasons which were never given, the Nigerian appointment was withdrawn and instead I was asked if I would accept one in Ghana. 'The White Man's grave!' exclaimed my mother raising her hands in horror. 'You surely won't accept.' At that time I would have accepted an appointment anywhere on earth.

FACETS OF FORESTY

Men like Thompson, McLeod, King-Church, Brent, Garnett, Arnold and Greene, who pioneered the forest service up to fifty years ago, to the middle-distance foresters such as myself, who joined the service in the late thirties, are ghosts in a shadowy past. Little is known of them; all but one or two are dead. The end-point of their work—the permanent forest estate—stands as a living memorial to them. The latter-day foresters traversing the boundaries which the pioneers cut and which generations of Forest Guards—some of the loneliest men in the world—have kept clear, might occasionally ponder as they walk in relative comfort, the sweat-pouring exertions of these pioneers as they selected, surveyed and cut these boundaries. These men for the most part knew not the comfort of a well-appointed bungalow on their return from the bush; for many there were no bungalows; they lived in bare resthouses or native houses of daub and wattle. For them there were no fans to cool the long hot airless nights; no refrigerators to cool the mud-tasting water after it had been boiled and filtered; no radio to lighten their loneliness. No wives.

If they fell sick, they usually doctored themselves. Doctors were few and available only in the towns. Transport was scarce and roads infrequent and often impassable in the rains. In the north of the forest zone rain is moderate and is usually fairly evenly distributed over seven months in the year. A completely dry month is rare. In the south-west, in the rain forest, rain falls most of the year, and for half of it, heavily. Solitary life in a tent or a bush hut, with only six-weeks-old newspapers to keep one in touch with reality, and living mainly out of tins, was trying. When tobacco went mouldy, as it did a day or two after the tin was opened, when bed linen was palpably damp as one crawled beneath the sheets, when the tea tasted of mould and one ran out of tinned milk, life became unpleasant.

When I began my service in 1938, L. C. Rowney was in charge of the Western Province. I knew little of him except that he drilled his Forest Guards like soldiers, for I was attached to him only for a couple of weeks. But I recall, vividly, the gaffe which I perpetrated which cannot have endeared him to me. I was unaware then, and have rarely observed since, the custom of sleeping on Saturday and Sunday afternoons. It has always seemed to me to be a waste of time. Shortly after I arrived in Sekondi, the provincial headquarters and once the main port of Ghana, and was quartered in one of the ' sweat boxes ' in the circle, a tiny cube of a bungalow, hot and airless, I ran out of reading material. It was a Saturday afternoon and not knowing that shops closed on a Saturday I walked the mile and a half into Sekondi town in search of something to read. It seemed a town of the dead. Retracing my steps I began to climb up the hill back to the bungalow. Half-way up, I paused to wipe my head and the inside of my helmet dry, and caught sight of the turning-off to Rowney's bungalow. I followed the road which looks down on the sea and climbing the rickety wooden steps, knocked. There was no answer. I knocked again. From within came a noise like a groan, a shuffle of foot-steps and Rowney's head, dishevelled and toothless, appeared. ' Excuse me, sir,' I said, ' I wonder if you have a book I could bor-row? ' Rowney's mouth opened and shut like that of a fish. His eyes closed momentarily as though with pain. I know now what he must have thought then. ' Come in and help yourself,' he mut-tered and shuffled back to the bedroom to resume his broken sleep. I heard Mrs Rowney's voice soothing him, I have no doubt. I selected a book and crept away guiltily. Later I apologized.

On the following Monday I attended bright and early at his office. This was situated as close to the sea as human ingenuity and regard for safety could contrive. Not as close as head office in

Accra, which is practically among the breakers, or the Cape Coast office, which is part of the historic castle above the dungeons whence the wretched slaves were driven into the waiting boats almost vertically below, but close enough to be pleasant. I was supposed to be of assistance to Rowney and also to acquaint myself with General, Financial and Standing Orders. As I was perusing one of these, the telephone rang. I lifted the receiver. 'cwp here,' came a staccato voice. I was used to the telephone. 'Collins, Forestry Department here,' I replied, having no idea who 'cwp' might be. The practice of abbreviating as many things, persons and institutions as possible, to the bare bones of their initials, was then only in its infancy and was new to me. pwd I knew, acf I knew—I was one—cfao, scoa and utc were vaguely recognizable as firms. All were constantly bandied about. Who in the tropics would want to bother with 'Compagnie Française Afrique Occidentale' when four letters were adequate? How was I to know that cwp meant the Hon. Commissioner (S. W. Saxton, Paymaster Commander (Ret)) for Western Province?

There was a snort at the other end of the wire. Back came the cwp's voice, raised I thought. 'Young man,' it said, 'you had better be careful. When you speak to me I expect you to say " sir ". After what happened on Friday you seem to have made the worst possible start here. Ask Mr Rowney to speak to me.' I explained that Mr Rowney was not in and could I take a message. There was another snort and a click at the other end and I hung up the receiver and went back to my General Orders. Friday's events, as far as I was concerned, had been unexpected and brief.

Even in December, 1938, preparations against possible enemy attack were being made and on that Friday a blackout was to be practised. No one had thought of informing me, a newcomer, of this fact and when the blackout should have been complete two lights were brightly burning on the ridge. One was mine. Deep in a book, I was oblivious of what was going on until a screech of brakes betokened the sudden arrival of a car. There came the sound of hurried footsteps approaching and a raucous voice bellowed from outside the door : 'Commissioner's compliments and will you please put out that bloody light.' Obediently I put it out. Conscious of a vague mutter from the rediffusion loudspeaker on the sideboard, I walked across and turned up the volume. 'There is still one light showing on the ridge,' a voice declared. 'The blackout is being spoiled because of one light. Please *put it out*! ' I learned later that the speaker was the District Commissioner Kerr and often wondered what he said when it was discovered that the light he referred to was his own! When Rowney came in I recounted the events of the morning. He grinned, informed me what CWP stood for, and told me not to worry

Two years later at Tamale, I met a Dr McLean with whom I played golf, unaware that he was the Hon. Commissioner for Western Province's new son-in-law. Later, I was relating at a party at which he also was present the story which was current in the south of the CWP's efforts to camouflage Elmina Castle against enemy attack, heaven knows why. Unfortunately, so the story went, work was begun on the landward side and they ran out of paint before the vital seaward walls could be treated. No more paint was available. I was aware of an air of unusual quiet as I told this story, still smarting a bit at Saxton's cavalier treatment of me, and it was not until an unbearable peak of embarrassment was reached that someone whispered in a voice audible to the entire company that the Hon. Commissioner's son-in-law was sitting next to me!

Rowney soon passed from our ken to take up a war appointment in England. He had intended to return, but having made one effort to do so and being torpedoed for his pains, he considered it safer to remain in England. He did not return to the Coast.

Early in 1939, I was posted to Ashanti and took charge of Juaso Forest District from George Cansdale. I recall that George spent most of his time during the take-over period in mounting a seemingly endless series of small mammals in which he was particularly interested. So engrossed was he that I had to prepare his annual report for him, although my knowledge of the District and of the work was nil. Fortunately annual reports were then short, simple documents easily contained on a couple of sheets of typescript.

Although Cansdale remained with the Department throughout the war, his intense interest in, and wide knowledge of, the fauna, caused him to leave when he was offered the Superintendentship of Regent's Park. Our paths did not often cross in Ghana (we have met more often since) but on the few occasions on which I visited him, his bungalow was more a refuge for animals than human

beings. Parrots and monkeys were often in attendance at mealtimes, while around and beneath the bungalow were numerous
boxes and packing cases and flimsy-looking wire cages filled with
all manner of creatures from bush babies to baboons and menac-
ing mambas to benign-looking, but nevertheless deadly vipers
who when disturbed hissed with the intensity of a locomotive
letting off steam. His enthusiasm was inclined to dominate conversation and likely to disrupt mealtimes entirely. He and Charles
Taylor were the greatest team of gossipers I have ever had the
pleasure of meeting.

The Provincial Forest Officer, Ashanti, was the late 'Helen'
Wills. As a new officer I knew nothing and was often slow to learn,
yet throughout my three years' probation, most of it spent under
Helen, he was the personification of kindness and even his
rebukes, usually merited, were so couched as to render them
benign. Wills was an old 'Coaster', a 'bottle a day man' on his
day, but teetotal and a glutton for work in the bush. He had some
hard critics in the Department and none more violent in their
criticism than one or two total abstainers who really did not know
the man. He was the terror of Dunkwa during the years he was
stationed there and the bachelors and grass widowers would regard
his return from bush at the head of a long line of carriers, fined
almost to the bone—he was at best a slim man—with justifiable
trepidation. They were to suffer some late nights and heavy heads
before he led his carriers once again into the forest of the Western
Province. I never saw him the worse for wear, though he exercised
his enormous capacity for liquor and for co-ordinated physical
exercise several times in my presence. He was an all-round games
player and shone at soccer, cricket and tennis. He was also a formidable snooker player.

I was once his guest while passing through Kumasi on my way
to pay-out the remoter part of my District: each Forest Ranger
and his staff is paid at his Range headquarters once a month, thus
does the District Officer get to know his staff. Dinner was arranged
on the Saturday night at his bungalow for the two of us, meanwhile he took me to the European Club for 'a game of snooker'.

At 3 am we were still at the Club playing snooker. We had been
drinking steadily, but not copiously, since 6.30, and though none
of the company was drunk, we were not focussing very well, except

Helen Wills. We were now in a party of about a dozen men (I do not recall seeing a woman in the Club that evening; now, they often outnumber the men), all snooker players of varying degrees of skill, all talking volubly around the table. I had known none of them except Wills in the beginning, but long before we left, it seemed as though we had been bosom pals for years. Included in the party was the Colonel of the Regiment, a District Commissioner, the United Africa Company's motor engineer, an agricultural officer and a police officer. None of us had eaten since lunch, except a few salted groundnuts which the Club steward had provided some hours before; all of us wanted to eat, but Helen, who had invited everyone for dinner (8.30!), wanted to play snooker. By 3.45 am he was the only one who was physically capable of playing, whereupon he said it was time for dinner.

What his steward and cook thought as a convoy of a dozen cars roared into Helen's compound at 4 am and he promptly demanded ' chop for fourteen masters', I do not know. It was a tradition, then, among Coast servants that they met all their master's most unreasonable demands with a grin and a word of acquiescence, and it was a matter of pride to both master and servant that a meal ordered for 8.30 for two people should, miraculously, it seemed, be perfectly prepared and expanded for fourteen, eight hours later. We dined at 4.30 am and made our hurried departures as soon after as decency permitted. I remember it was almost light as I tumbled wearily into bed, conscious that I had a game of tennis to play with Helen at 7.30 am. I was awakened by my boy at 7 am and Helen and I were on the court before 7.30, whereupon he proceeded to thrash me 6.0, 6.0, 6.0. I rather fancied myself as an above average attacking player, but Helen, nearly twenty years my senior, almost ran me off the court. You may recall that Miss Helen Wills was still a Wimbledon idol in those days.

During the war years, I was in and out of the Army twice within a few months, unlike most of my brother officers who served throughout the East African and Burma campaigns. I served in Ashanti throughout the early war years and got to know and to like Helen Wills. He was a fragile-looking, soft-spoken man, a great Church-goer with a softer spot for the African than many of his contemporaries. In anger, which was rare, he was a terror:

cold, clipped, bitingly sarcastic and strangely bitter. Generally he was a gentle man, helpful and easy to get on with.

There was little forestry work done during the war for not only did we not have the staff, but our preoccupation was with supply work. Like coals to Newcastle, wood had actually been imported into Ghana for many years: most of the old bungalows and offices had ceilings, floors and doors of imported pitch pine. Many of these have been replaced, or the buildings themselves knocked down, or even fallen down, for the resin-scented pine is *hors d'oeuvre* to the termite accustomed to sharpening his jaws on tasteless hardwood. Suddenly, Ghana had to produce all the timber she needed locally and for export. The sawmill capacity was slight and emphasis was laid on the traditional means of rendering wood into boards and scantlings, pitsawing.

The Department's excursion into the esoteric world of saw-milling, had not been an entirely happy one. Helen Wills early in his service had found himself almost in sole charge of an outfit whose purpose was to demonstrate efficient and economical milling to the trade. At that time (1920-1923) we had neither the proper machinery nor the trained staff to operate it and we were soon glad to hand it over to private enterprise. Nor did private enterprise thrive; the mill concerned has chugged slowly on, driven by great steam boilers of low efficiency, and it has scarcely ever more than just paid its way. It was some years later that we were able to afford to recruit a Forest Engineer, George Cawood, who designed and built a mill in Kumasi which from its inception demonstrated that a mill built largely from odd bits and pieces found lying about the country could be made to work efficiently. Having demonstrated this, Government sold it to Messrs African Woods Ltd, who still operate it as one of the most efficient mills in Ghana. Cawood resigned his job to join hands with Bob Briscoe, at that time engaged in making a vast fortune out of sawmilling. Not many years afterwards Briscoe's mill designed by Cawood was also sold at a handsome profit and both men were until recently comfortably retired in South Africa.

It fell mainly to Wills to organize the pitsawing industry in Ashanti and this he did with considerable success. He will be remembered for many things he did: he could chew up a wine glass and swallow the pieces without suffering any ill effects, at the time, though it probably brought about his relatively early demise; his periodic hard drinking was well known; his athletic prowess even when approaching middle age was remarkable, and his church singing was harmonious if not gifted. Those of us who worked under him in Ashanti during the war years will also remember him for two quite unconnected achievements: the success of the Kumasi Timber Producers' Co-operative Society and his savings scheme.

Unions of any kind are still novel in Ghana, and in 1940, when the Kumasi Timber Producers' Co-operative Society first saw light of day, the idea was almost revolutionary. No one had tried, with any success, to weld the interests of large numbers of illiterate sawyers, who had never had any connection with the white man and rarely even saw him. As we gradually speeded up the tempo of pitsawing, whipping the pitsawyers' enthusiasm, if not to fever pitch, at least to the pitch where they worked a five-day week, some kind of scheme to organize and unify their efforts became necessary.

It is not many years since the last pitsawyers ceased work in Britain. In Ghana, prior to 1939, it was the chief method of sawing logs and could produce lumber more cheaply, and almost as good as, any existing mill. Over a million cubic feet of lumber are still pitsawn annually, a tiny proportion compared with the thirty million cubic feet that are mill-sawn, but nevertheless a sizeable cottage industry. The chief advantage which pitsawn has over mill-sawn lumber, is cheapness. At pitside it usually costs two or three shillings per cubic foot less than the machine-sawn product. The advantage of having the timber sawn near the consumer gives the pitsawyer another advantage. If a chief's palace is being built in a relatively remote spot, it is often possible to hire pitsawyers to produce the necessary timber near the site, and so save transport.

As we strove to stimulate the industry we utilized this advantage to the full and trees for pitsawing were selected as near to road and rail as possible. The other big advantage which pitsawing always has over mill-sawing is that few capital assets are needed. A sawmill, to be profitable, must be run as hard as possible, to utilize fully the employees who are paid whether or not timber is sawn. The pitsawyer is usually also a farmer who does his sawing when he is not farming. He can always stop without financial calamity. Often, he saws on a contract basis supplying one-third of the lumber he cuts in return for a free tree from the owner, and selling the remaining two-thirds for his own profit. His tools are a saw, a penny ruler and a piece of string.

The usual defects of pitsawn timber would cause its rejection from a sawmill. Variation in thickness, width and length, are often considerable; sapwood is often left on to attract the wood-borers and destructive fungi. But the demand is maintained. The tree when felled is cross-cut into twelve, fourteen or sixteen feet lengths, depending on the terms of the contract which will demand lumber in one or more of those lengths, or on local custom. A pit is meanwhile dug slightly longer and wider than the largest log which is then rolled over the pit to rest on stout poles. The log is then sawn lengthways down the middle, one sawyer standing in the pit, the other on top of the log, the long wooden-handled pitsaw being pulled down by the former and hauled up by the latter. A piece of string soaked in a mixture of charcoal and water is used first as a plumb-line, held taut across the end of the log, pulled and released like a bow string, thereby implanting a black line on the cross-cut end. This guides the sawyers in their initial cut; a good eye does the rest. A good eye may dispense entirely with this aid and I have seen logs apparently machine-cut by eye. Indeed, the makers of sea-going canoes who hollow them from the immense logs of Wawa, often use no measuring instruments, yet these craft which are wonderful sea boats and are practically unsinkable lie sweetly on an even keel when they are introduced to the sea a hundred or more miles away.

Each log is treated separately over the pit, the dimensions of the boards and scantlings being marked with the wet charcoal string after having been measured with the ruler. One cannot profitably hurry pitsawing (or any kind of handsawing for that matter) without sacrificing accuracy and achieving exhaustion; consequently the apparently leisurely pace which the sawyers adopt is at or near the optimum for economic production. A good gang, three or four in number, will work virtually non-stop throughout the day-light hours without seeming to exert themselves. A well-matched pair can go on without ceasing for the whole length of a log. Much depends on the saw, the wood and the matching of the pair. There are no efficient saw doctors outside the milling industry today and during the war years, few in it. When a pitsaw is blunted, the sawyer knows roughly only how to file it sharp again; he has no knowledge of setting or tempering. The traditional wood of the pitsawyer is Odum (Iroko), which until the last war was almost the only wood used. It is durable, resistant even to termite attack, strong, and grows to an enormous size by African standards. The biggest I ever saw measured thirty-eight feet girth breast height and had a straight unbroken stem for at least a hundred feet. Royalties are fixed 'per tree', so that it usually pays to select the biggest. This is not always so, for the labour and cost of carrying the lumber out of the forest is no insignificant item and a small tree near a road may be worth more than a giant deep in the forest.

Many Odum trees contain stone, deposits of calcium carbonate which may give the sawn wood a limed effect and often renders it so hard that I have known some massive trees abandoned before a single log was sawn. I once bought a board from one such tree and found it so hard with stone that it was like working a piece of marble. I expect, twenty years after, that the termites are still blunting their jaws on it.

For furniture, joinery and building in general, there are a dozen species whose royalties are lower, which are easier to shape and finish and sufficiently durable for the purpose. As we organized the pitsawyers during the war, they forsook their traditional wood for easier and more profitable ones. Mahogany and cedars were much in demand, while for railway sleepers the more resistant Baku, Dahoma and Kusia were employed. As imports were reduced, often to a trickle if a convoy happened to be badly mauled, as they often were on 'U-boat corner', rounding the bulge of Africa, we had either to do without or find substitutes. Until the war Ghana was roofed with corrugated iron. Imports of this soon ceased and the shingle-splitting industry was resuscitated.

Such mundane but essential things as sacks and jute for wrapping and packing rubber, also disappeared from the market. The bark-cloth beaters were soon busy hammering the bast of the Kyenkyen tree into tough, strong bark cloth which found a ready market. Luxuries such as honey and jam were always in short supply. My cook made my jam from the red fruits of the Pitanga

Cherry hedge I planted, and when I could get no sugar, I decided that we would harvest the product of the wild bee.

The honey and wax industry, which reached respectable proportions later in the war, though it never even approached the scale of the industry as practised in Tanganyika or even Nigeria, nevertheless was worth while. It began over a drink in Dr Macpherson's bungalow. I cannot recall why I was there drinking his beer. Macpherson like so many of his countrymen, was a crusty, abrupt individual, but kind. The subject of bees arose, heaven knows why, and Macpherson mentioned that he had a complete bee-keeping outfit in his store which he had never found time to use. When I told him that I was a bee-keeper and could find time to employ his equipment, he promptly made me a gift of the lot. Counting the hive, wax sheets, of which there were several hundred, frames, smoker, separators and a spare super, it was a valuable gift and it contributed to the war effort to the tune of several tons of honey, most of which went to the Royal Air Force, as recounted in *The Perpetual Forest*.

I had started bee-keeping because of a similar unsolicited gift. A friend of my father offered me his fully-stocked hive, ostensibly in return for a gigantic marrow which my father had grown and which, at his behest, I had carried half-way up a Welsh mountainside. It was a fine Sunday morning and having gladly delivered the giant I sat on the lawn drinking lemonade not a stone's throw from a beehive. Deciding, perhaps, that it wished to share the sweetness of my drink, a bee, quite by accident, stung me. Shortly afterwards my father's friend enquired if I was interested in bees, ' because if you are ' he said ' you can have this hive '. I wasn't very interested at that moment, but the opportunity of really owning a hive of live bees was too good to miss and I prevaricated when I said I was interested. Less than twenty-four hours later, at dawn, I gently wheeled the hive down the hill in a borrowed wheelbarrow and thus became a bee-keeper. I have never lost the fascination of bees and a kind of reverence for their selfless organization, cleanliness and efficiency.

With Dr Macpherson's hive I was in a position to demonstrate bee-keeping, and incidentally, to keep myself in honey for many years in Africa. It takes a hive of bees the equivalent of twenty pounds of honey to make one pound of wax, so if one wants a fair return of honey it is necesssary to provide the bees with wax in a form which they will accept. The form they accept comprises thin sheets of bees-wax imprinted with the outline of the hexagonal cell. The sheets of foundation are wired into vertically hanging frames within the hive and the bees draw out the imprinted hexagonal outlines until they have made individual cells. It saves them considerable time and energy which they then proceed to put into the collection and ripening of nectar to produce honey.

It was Fabre, I think, who stated a century ago that so accurate were hive bees that the hexagonal cell which they built could be taken as a standard of measurement. The West African honey bee is a fraction smaller than his cousin of Europe, from whom I believe he is descended, via the golden-ringed bees of the ancient Egyptians, who kept bees in clay pots in the walls of their houses, presumably to serve a dual purpose. I wondered if the smaller African bee would adapt the larger celled foundation. To find out I first had to obtain a swarm or colony of local bees.

My first colony was brought in at dead of night after considerable labour. A hive had been discovered living in a fallen tree some miles away in the forest. News of this did not reach me until late afternoon and by the time our party of a Forest Ranger, two labourers and myself had reached the spot, dusk was falling. The fallen tree was a small one, not more than eighteen inches in diameter, but it took us hours to saw through it for it was ebony; by which time we had all been stung by returning bees unable to enter the hive since for our own protection we had plugged the entrance hole. When we had sawn off a four feet length we staggered homewards through the darkness with the log on our shoulders.

I am astonished that we ever got the log home for our single torch gave up the ghost long before we reached the road. It was a nightmare journey, but mercifully a short one. For much of the time the heavy log took charge of us like a battering ram hurtling us forward in short mad rushes that we were powerless to stop. I had instructed that on no account should the log be dropped, nor was it. All to no purpose alas, for on the morrow at first light when I opened the hive I discovered, as I had feared after the night's rough handling, that the colony had 'balled' the queen and there were few survivors.

Above: James Town, Accra. *Below:* The Golden Pods.

The tangle of the high forest.

A bridge party was responsible for my first live colony of West African bees. I was invited from Juaso to play with the Gibsons at Konongo Gold Mines seven miles away. It was a Saturday and I spent most of the afternoon in the Mine's pool, enjoying the cold water pumped up from the lower levels of the workings hundreds of feet below. Over tea at my hosts' bungalow, Ina Gibson remarked that there was a swarm of bees in the hibiscus hedge nearby. I promptly deserted tea and with the aid of a pair of secateurs, a small box and the tail of one of Bill Gibson's old shirts, soon had the swarm neatly housed.

Thereupon Ina's interest in the Hymenoptera evaporated and she refused to have the box anywhere in their bungalow. Next door lived Dr Dyce-Sharpe, a good friend of mine; he was tragically drowned at sea a few weeks later. From his cook I obtained a little sugar, made up a solution of it in water and poured some of it on to the shirt tail which covered the box. From within came an instantaneous murmur, which swiftly mounted to a hum of appreciation as hundreds of long tongues began to probe the shirting and suck up the sugary solution. The doctor was taken aback when later he returned and opened the box to discover bees, fortunately gorged and contented with sugar.

'Jam' was the local name for wild honey and it sold for a shilling a beer bottle. It was obtained by hunters who, when they discovered a hive of bees in a tree, destroyed the colony with smoke and fire. The shattered and blackened combs with their contents of eggs, brood, young bees, raw nectar, honey and pollen, were then squeezed in a piece of old cloth and the resulting liquid run into a bottle and sold. A jam, the dictionary tells us, is the result of a squeeze and this doubtful-looking concoction was not thus foisted on the public under false pretences. If you could stomach it, and most Ghanaians could, then I imagine that it must be the nearest thing to an elixir yet devised.

As the U-boat menace tightened its grip on the outward-bound convoys, as the garrisons of troops, gunners, Navy and Air Force increased, the demand for such things as sugar became far greater than the supply and though there was no official rationing, we all were rationed nevertheless. However nutritious the locally-produced 'jam' may have been with its rich extract of protein in the form of dead squashed larvae and pollen, the demand for it

TWB   D

remained strictly local. The first problem was to organize the
collection and storage of clean honey. Courses in apiculture were
given to suitable young men and attempts were made to introduce
planned bee-keeping, employing locally-made hives and methods
of extraction which did not annihilate the bees. At the same time I
encouraged the young bee-keepers to use controlled smoking when
taking honey from wild hives, but I had little success in any of
these ventures and practically none when it came to convincing
hunters that by employing their age-old method of killing the bees
by fire and smoke they were slowly killing the goose that laid the
golden eggs.

Constant propaganda by the travelling apiculturists soon saw a
vast improvement in the quality and quantity of wild honey.
Watered honey is not always easy to detect at once, but if it is kept
a few days it will ferment. Supplies were therefore stored for a few
days before payment was made. All honey when it had proved
itself was strained and stored in wax-lined clay pots produced
locally for 3d each. Soon honey was flowing by the ton. Dr Macpherson's hive was also producing a regular supply of honey in
combs besides being used as a demonstration hive. So much honey
was flowing that it became necessary to obtain larger and less
fragile containers for it. The Royal Air Force was taking it by the
hundredweight and it was not very satisfactory to fill and despatch
such quantities in five-pound clay pots. The Konongo Gold Mines
obtained their supplies of sulphuric acid, used in the extraction
of gold, in stout twenty-gallon glass demijohns each encased in a
rubber-cushioned wooden crate. In normal times these were
returnable and were refilled in England and despatched again and
again to the Coast. At this time there was no shipping space and
I discovered about two hundred of these apparently of no use to
anyone lying outside the power house. I enquired if they were
available and how much they would cost. I was informed I could
have them for nothing providing I could obtain transport to
remove them. Joyously I removed them the same day, for as a
Forest Officer I controlled the issue of petrol to timber haulers,
and one of them was only too pleased to lend me his lorry 'to help
the war effort'.

As honey containers the demijohns were ideal, easily cleaned,
filled and emptied, and, in their rubber-cushioned crates, almost

unbreakable. Twenty gallons of honey in a clear glass jar is a beautiful sight. With a light behind it it glows like liquid gold shot with fire. Before I knew it the jars were in great demand for electric-light stands, and not all of them came back empty in spite of a high surcharge. There must be scores of these demijohn lamp stands giving joy to their owners all over the world. I should like one myself!

I should like to report that all this effort developed the industry. Alas, it did not and the only honey one can now obtain from the forest is the same old ' jam ' sold in a beer bottle. The only thing different is the price; it is now 2s 6d a bottle.

From Juaso I was transferred to Sunyani where I took my hives, now numbering three, two having been made by local carpenters as fair copies of the original and populated with captured swarms. The local bees in spite of their size tailored the English wax foundation to their liking and seemed happy in their clean new homes.

Soon, however, a dreadful scourge appeared : the wax moth. In England I knew the wax moth to be a pest which was practically endemic to every hive. It is a nuisance but rarely becomes a serious pest in a well-run apiary. The West African wax moth is a giant by comparison. The adult moth itself is small and dun-coloured and the female sidles past the guard bees through the hive entrance and in the darkness of the hive makes her cringing way to the combs. On these she lays her eggs and dies. The eggs soon hatch into tiny larvae which feed on the wax and the cell contents, growing as they feed, their appetites increasing as they grow. Bigger, much bigger, than their temperate cousins, they writhe their horrible way over and through the combs, destroying them and leaving death and destruction in their wake. The bees are quite unable to deal with them, although they would soon sting to death any bee or wasp marauder who invaded their home and entomb its body so that it should not contaminate the hive. Finally, no combs remain, the army of writhing larvae pupates and the bees either perish miserably or desert the hive.

During a long absence in the bush, the wax moth invaded my hives and when I returned I found all the hives empty of bees and full of wax-moth larvae. I was soon busy hunting new swarms. The Chief Conservator asked me to include a course of Apiculture in the Forest Rangers' training school of which I was in charge and the Learners were as pleased as I was when we began bee-keeping in earnest. The local Government school then showed interest and I donated two hives complete with colonies which were installed in the school grounds. One of the senior boys who seemed particularly keen was also trained to handle the bees, but in spite of a complete suit of protective clothing, which encased him from head to toe, not forgetting his hands, he never developed the confidence necessary to become a practising bee-keeper as the following incident illustrates.

I had gone on leave, married and had brought my bride to Sunyani as part of a sight-seeing tour which I thought she should have, as I thought there might not be such an opportunity again, nor has there been. The Deputy Chief Conservator (W. T. S. Brown) did not approve of this local leave, designed as it was to traverse the whole of the forest zone, some 1,500 miles in fourteen days. Just after the war we were allowed this much local leave and I intended to make the most of mine as it did not seem likely that the opportunity would recur. Brown's argument was that an average of just over a hundred miles a day was not 'leave' and I was likely to return more exhausted than refreshed. This ignored the fact that I had recently purchased a new eight-cylinder Super-de-luxe Ford saloon, capable of smooth travel up to 90 mph and that a hundred miles a day, did not, even on poor roads, represent more than three hours' travel. We have, in fact, never travelled so comfortably since in a series of progressively smaller English cars, culminating in a 600 cc Fiat 'bus' which accommodates my family of five very well.

Fortunately, the Chief Conservator, 'Steve', had better perspective and overrode his Deputy. We had our trip and Sunyani provided the hightlight. De Sautoy, lately Director of the Department of Social Welfare and Community Development, was the District Commissioner at the time and staying with him was an Education officer whose name I cannot recall. They both ran as for their lives on that day. One of my first visits was to the Government School and the hives. The latter seemed to be fairly bursting with bees and I reckoned that they should contain a good harvest of honey. The headmaster admitted that none of them had been touched since I had left about a year before. I enquired of my star bee pupil and gathered that in spite of his bee suit he was 'much too feared' to tackle the hives alone.

We arranged to open the hives that afternoon at about 4.30 pm. We arrived on the scene to find a hundred and fifty schoolchildren and their friends assembled around the hive at a respectful distance. On our way we met De Sautoy and his friend and they too came along.

With bees, familiarity never breeds contempt. Familiarity is an essential part of the bee-keepers know-how and a complete absence of fear is a pre-requisite. To no animal is fear so obvious as to the bee. Relying on keen scent for its livelihood, it is quick to sense the smell of fear because it can approach closely and swiftly. The smell of fear is the sharp odour which enhances that of normal sweat and which cannot be disguised or controlled. I had only once known fear with bees and suffered a terrible chain reaction of stings as a result which made me ill. Working without veil or gloves I had been attacked by several bees as I approached the hive. There may have been some obnoxious odour about me such as carbolic soap or brussels sprouts or tobacco. At any rate I was stung several times as I began my examination of the hive. As I turned back the quilt which covered the top of the brood chamber I viewed the combs covered with a dark seething mass of bees. Suddenly I felt frightened, conscious that my face had no protection. Swiftly and gently I replaced the quilt and began to put on the hive roof. As I did so the hive erupted with hundreds of angry bees. Dropping the roof I ran, escaping indoors with only twenty or thirty stings. I replaced the hive roof late that night! The following day I had to force myself to re-open the same hive, wondering whether there would be a repetition of the previous day's performance. I was afraid all right, not so much for myself, for I wore veil and gloves and my flannel trousers were well tucked-in my socks, but afraid of being afraid, realizing that I should be a failure as a bee-keeper if I lost confidence. Fortunately the bees were docile. I never had a recurrence of this fear, and I was ever afterwards careful to be immaculately clean and free from any artificial odour whenever I handled bees.

My bee pupil arrived clad in his bee suit and while Bette and I stood near the first hive, he began, under my instruction, to examine and manipulate the hive. We lit the smoker, a metal funnel filled with brown corrugated paper and attached to a small hand-operated bellows. This is the time honoured means of mildly panicking the bees, causing them to run to the honey combs and gorge themselves in the fear, so we believe, that the hive is being threatened and should its desertion be necessary the honey stocks must be saved at all costs. I told the boy to give two or three gentle puffs at the hive entrance. The colony was strong and from within we could hear the deep sonorous murmur of a happy, vigorous hive. The scent of the hive was the wonderful combination of honey and new wax, one of nature's finest perfumes and known only to the bee and the bee-keeper. While the smoke was taking effect we waited. The song of the hive grew louder as the bees, frightened by the irritation of the smoke, their age-long enemy, plundered the honey combs; soon the hive was almost vibrating with the murmur of a ten-thousand strong choir.

It was a hot afternoon and the boy clad in his protective clothes sweated; as he sweated he trembled slightly.

'Now take off the roof, *gently*,' I emphasized, and repeated the word. Gently the roof came off though it had been heavily propolized. Beneath was a strip of linen which I had placed there over a year before to cover the frames. A few bees crawled out to investigate. 'Give them a little smoke,' I whispered. He did so and the frightened creatures scurried downwards. The sound of the hive was now like a muted church organ.

We waited a little longer.

'Now lift the super, *very gently*,' I told him.

The super is the box above the brood chamber and in a vigorous colony in good bee country as many as six supers may be put on to provide plenty of storage room for the nectar and honey. Lack of room will cause the bees to swarm. If the super were full of honey, as I thought it might be, it would weigh anything up to thirty pounds and, in view of the heavy propolizing evident on top of the frames, it would require considerable gentle prising to separate it from the brood chamber below. The boy was as big and probably as strong as I; I thought he could do it. For a minute or two the sweating boy wrestled quietly with the super. Bees were now flying in their thousands about us. The crowd moved back. There was, however, no harm in the bees. Most of them were gorged with honey and were happy; the others took their cue from the happy ones. I whispered patience and gentleness to the boy. A sudden jolt would certainly anger the bees.

Suddenly, the super was torn loose with a rending of linen and propolis. An eruption of bees shot upwards and, in sudden panic, the boy dropped the super. Had he replaced it and retired, all would have been well. But he dropped it and ran. Ten thousand furious bees followed him. The crowd needed no starter's orders; it dispersed rapidly and within seconds there was not a soul to be seen. De Sautoy and his friend disappeared with the rest. Not wishing to be stung to death we stood quietly by while the tumult and the shouting died rapidly in the distance. When the bees had quietened down and were concentrating on licking up the honey which was trickling from the broken combs I gently replaced the super, put on the roof and returned unscathed to the rest-house.

Forest Officers were Rubber Officers too. With the fall of Malaya, Britain was hard put to obtain rubber for such essentials as tyres. In Ghana there were millions of wild rubber trees (*Funtumia elastica*). Many had been tapped in the boom years just after the first world war when rubber became an important export commodity. Some of the trees still showed the herring-bone pattern of tapping cuts, long since healed with callus. A multitude of climbers and wild fig trees had also contributed rubber and provided rubber adulterants in earlier days. *Landolphia* rubber from the massive thigh-thick climber which writhes in vast reptilian fantasy through the high forest was marketed in balls called 'Krepi Ball', 'Accra Niggers' or 'Addah Niggers' and commanded a high price. Many plants yield latex (families Moraceae, Euphorbiaceae and Apocynaceae chiefly) when slashed but few of them produce a rubber on coagulating which has a commercial value.

We encouraged the dying art of tapping and discouraged, with little success, the practice of adulteration. The specific gravity of latex is similar to that of water and the addition of water to latex in moderate quantities could not be detected until after it had been coagulated and the amount of rubber determined. Tappers insisted on cash payments for their latex. Most latex was collected in four-gallon petrol and kerosene tins which almost entirely took the place of buckets throughout Africa even before the war. There

were no petrol pumps between towns and few in the towns before
the war and if we were embarking on a long journey we carried
our own petrol in four-gallon tins, neatly boxed in pairs. The
empty tins were worth about 3d. My cook used one as an oven when
I went to bush and baked bread in it that would have shamed the
modern British baker. As the tempo of the war increased, the
wooden boxes disappeared; then tins became scarce and petrol
came in forty-gallon drums. Finally, supplies of steel were eked
out by making the few tins that could be made with a high lead
content which made them dangerous for cooking and storing
drinking water. Notices were plastered everywhere drawing attention to this fact.

Apart from the dilution of latex with water and the addition of
adulterants, even flour, to thicken watered latex, a trick which
deceived the rubber buyers for a long time, was a reduction in
the capacity of the four-gallon petrol tin. This was accomplished
by lightly beating the sides of the tins with a thin stick, thereby
reducing their capacity by a couple of pints. Two pints in thirty-
two was not much, but where brokers were dealing in thousands
of tins, thousands of pints meant an appreciable gain for
the unscrupulous tappers and a corresponding loss for the
brokers.

A few plantations of Para rubber, the rubber of commerce,
existed, and these were tapped in the accepted fashion by periodically paring a thin shaving of callus from the edge of the old tapping wound and allowing the latex to drip into an empty cup,
usually an empty milk tin, hung on a nail below. By this means
regular monthly tapping could be undertaken throughout the life
of the tree. In the forest, a different system had to be adopted. Here
was no plantation with large rubber trees in orderly lines, where
each individual tapping takes place near ground-level and takes
only a few seconds. The *Funtumia* trees are scattered haphazardly
throughout the forest. The seed of the tree is borne on a tiny hair-
like parachute which is widely dispersed and so are the trees
which grow from these seeds. First, the tapper had to find his trees
and then memorize a rough pattern of their distribution. So
scattered are the trees that to gather an economic yield it was
necessary to spend a day or two in the bush. Moreover, the *Funtumia* tree is a small tree and its yield if tapped conventionally

would only be a few drops of latex. Thus an annual tapping was done, and the *whole* tree trunk was tapped. This involved climbing the tree as high as a man could climb. To expedite this, the tapper wore a climbing harness comprising a pair of stirrups and a rope which encircled the trunk, made of tough palm fibre. With this the tapper, knife in belt, could haul himself up by hands and feet in relative safety. As he climbed, he cut a herring-bone pattern in the trunk, leading into a central deep 'backbone' which allowed the white latex to trickle into a container, a milk tin, or more usually, a cup of leaves, on the ground. A large *Funtumia* might take him upwards for seventy to eighty feet. A skilled tapper might take an hour to complete the tapping of such a tree. More often, the tree was much smaller and could be finished in a few minutes. Working from dawn to dark the earnest tapper, out to make a sizeable sum of money, would tap some twenty to thirty trees a day and collect about four gallons of latex. This was stored in petrol tins, or in a larger drum and head-loaded or rolled to the nearest buying centre, anything up to fifty miles away.

It was a fairly lucrative, but arduous and dangerous business. More than one tapper failed to return to his hut, his harness breaking and his body being broken in the fall. More than one luckless man fell and was impaled on the spear-like growing point of a palm-tree below, there to lie screaming in agony, till death by haemorrhage or ants released him. More than one tapper died from a severed femoral artery, caused when the razor-sharp tapping knife slipped, leaving him to bleed swiftly to death, his body hanging in his harness till he was found. Sometimes it was never found. A body and its bones soon disintegrate in the damp heat of the forest even when not aided by driver ants who can clean the flesh from the bones of a human body overnight.

Shortage of steel infused new life into the shingle-cutting industry and new houses and huts with wooden shingle roofs added a touch of quality to the usual drab village scene with its acres of rusting corrugated iron. Nails, like all ferrous products, were desperately short so we introduced wooden pegs for fixing the shingles. Millions of the latter were split and purchased and huge stocks were held by forestry offices all over the country and caused endless headaches as the numbers counted in boards of survey never agreed with those recorded in the store ledgers. The same applied to pieces of timber. Although the timber stacks were enclosed with barbed wire and watchmen were employed, my books invariably showed a deficiency.

Kumasi, the capital town of Ashanti, centred in the forest zone, dealt with most of the pitsawn timber and thousands of boards and scantlings came in monthly by headload, on lorries and by train, to be checked, counted, paid for and stacked and subsequently issued to whatever Government Department or private firm required them. There were more than a thousand pitsawyers in Ashanti, each gang of two or three, producing a board or two each day, each being regularly exhorted to produce more ' for the war effort '. The organization which Helen Wills built up from nothing into the Kumasi Timber Producers' Association was necessary to maintain order and preserve our sanity.

Transport and tools were prerequisites. The former involved not only petrol, of which there was never enough, but tyres and lorries themselves, all of which required permits which were issued only on merit. The black market in Ghana was doubly black and the timber market and the producers concerned thrived only because there was protection from upscrupulous storekeepers who sometimes boosted the prices of their goods a hundred-fold. The formation of the Association gave the illiterate pitsawyers a fair crack of the whip. Prices were controlled, tools were made readily available and by selling their lumber to the Association they obtained not only prompt, but the proper payment and advances for the purchase of tools as well as permits to enable them to buy the tools.

The smooth running of such an organization, unique in the annals of trading in Ghana, based as it was on reciprocal trust, was not achieved without difficulties and the use of considerable tact. Much of the credit for the conception of the Association and the efficiency with which it functioned was due to Wills' single-minded enthusiasm and his willingness to treat the African as an equal.

He will be remembered for that, and for his Savings Campaign. The latter he imposed on us by constantly nagging at the necessity for saving to speed ' the war effort '. He bore down so heavily on us all, by word and letter, from the most junior Forest Guard to the most senior Assistant Conservator of Forests, that for peace's sake as much as anything we all subscribed to the savings fund. The results were astonishing and by the end of the war, Forest Guards who otherwise might not have saved a penny, found themselves holding Savings Certificates to the value of a whole year's salary.

Helen Wills, like most of the old Coasters, has gone. A sudden internal haemorrhage killed him before he had had time to enjoy his retirement; maybe his hard drinking plus his strange habit of eating glass, had something to do with his end. His epitaph, as that of so many old Coasters who sacrificed their youth and vigour in heat and loneliness, is that he worked hard and played hard, and if the bottle loomed larger in his play than in that of some others, he was 'no less a man for a' that'.

The Department had more than its share of characters and a reputation for integrity and devotion to duty unsurpassed in a Service where there have usually been no rigid hours; where 'shop' was talked at all hours of the day, anywhere; where Sundays were often working days. We were an efficient and proud organization which worked hard and played no less assiduously.

What is it that makes a Forester? In my case it was largely the lack of a job. In most other cases I know it was dedication to a life which allowed considerable freedom of action, of independence, and a love of the outdoors. Among my contemporaries there was a singular lack of high ambition that might perhaps be equated with a high degree of clodhopping. The assumption has no foundation. With rare exceptions the Forest Officers I have known have been content in their jobs, deriving considerable satisfaction from doing the job well and possessing fewer inhibitions and nursing fewer grievances than any comparable body of men anywhere. Their monetary reward has been adequate rather than exciting, with little chance of retiring higher than the rank of Conservator after twenty-five years impeccable service, and even less chance of collecting an award. No one to my knowledge below the rank of Chief Conservator ever did gain a civil award, though through no lack of recommendations. This could not be said of the Administrative Service, where devotion to a desk occasionally earned an MBE or OBE and with it galloping promotion. We technical officers were often irked at the sight of young District Commissioners, down still on their cheeks, taking up super-scale appointments in Accra. We grinned and muttered something about 'jobs for the boys', and griped about being 'in the wrong Department'. We were irked though certain to have the last laugh as the Administration was handed its bowler hat on the attainment of independence. Ghana would need its technicians yet awhile.

CHAPTER FOUR

Making a Forest Reserve

In a country where blood, that is, family, and land are still regarded as the most important things in life, any dealings in either must be conducted with great circumspection. Fifty years ago when forestry was begun, there was plenty of land. The population of the forest zone was no more than one million and there were about 25,000 square miles of forest land, little of it farmed. This meant sixteen acres for every man, woman and child. There was no land hunger. Even with all this land, little of it used, the reactions of the Chiefs, who are the custodians of the land, to forest reservation and the enactment of legislation to permit reservation, was violent and sustained.

Wisdom is easily acquired after the event and it is easy to point a finger and say, as one can, that it was lack of understanding by the Chiefs and their subjects which sustained the opposition to the forest laws. It was lack of understanding of this point, or indifference to it, or both, of which the Government was then guilty, and, as a result, was responsible for many of the difficulties which the Forestry Department suffered then and now. The Forests Ordinance, drafted in 1910, was not given legal sanction until seventeen years later! The resistance of the senior Chiefs and the intelligentsia obstructed its passage until a Commission of Enquiry was held and dissipated some of the misconceptions from which they suffered.

Shortly after the outbreak of the first world war, most of the Forestry staff volunteered for service and the Department was closed down. In 1919, it was resuscitated but still denied powers to put into effect a forest policy. There were no powers of reservation; no permanent forest estate, and no visible forest policy. There might as well have been no Forestry Department. Government, in conformity with its policy of indirect rule, maintained that the people should be allowed to choose whether or not Forest Reserves were to be created. This was tantamount to giving the United Nations' power of veto to schoolboys. Indirect rule was all very well, but this example of it was so indirect as to be valueless. The people were not going to give their land away, they were not even going to sell it, if they could help it. The result was that the Department was allowed to act in an advisory capacity only, and only those Native Authorities and Chiefs who could be persuaded would sign Bye-laws constituting their forest land as Forest Reserves. Understandably we had little success.

Such indirect rule, though applauded by the Chiefs and the intelligentsia, was not understood by them and was rarely practised. Years passed and the permanent forest estate which we knew was an essential basis, not merely for the practice of forestry, but for the continued prosperity of the whole country, facts which only now are being slowly appreciated by some politicians, was still as far from reality as it was when 'Timber' Thompson made his recommendations. The people and the Chiefs thought that Government intended to annex their land and so long as they were not forced to agree, they refused to have anything to do with forest reservation. The Government did little to remove this misconception.

In 1924, after repeated representations by the Conservator of Forests, the Governor at last put his foot down. His Excellency stated in an address before the Legislative Council: '... I deliberately adopted the method of trusting the Chiefs (in the passing and administration of Forest Reserve Bye-laws) and the people four years ago. I still repose my trust in them; but as the time for inaction has passed I have laid down the period during which I consider that my confidence should be justified. It now depends entirely on the Chiefs and their people as to whether the Forestry Ordinance shall be or shall not be passed during 1926 or 1927.' For the Foresters this was wonderful news.

His Excellency had pointed out that he was giving the Chiefs and their subjects two years in which to achieve reasonable progress in reservation and a further two years for administration according to the Bye-laws. Otherwise, he warned, an Ordinance would be passed which would give the Government powers of reservation without the people having a say in the matter. How much more indirect can rule by a colonial power become?

Do the people who shout against Imperialism recognize it?

The effect was momentarily startling and some 250 square miles of Forest Reserves were promptly constituted under Bye-laws. As though ashamed of their panic, the Chiefs did nothing more, and a year later it was evident that no further reservation was intended. The Governor kept his word. Promptly a Forests Ordinance was drafted and became law in March, 1927, seventeen years after the original ordinance had been shelved. 'Timber' Thompson's monumental treks had not been made in vain. The Ordinance did not preclude the passing of Native Bye-laws; it did, however, insist on reservation by one means or the other. The law was now on our side and sooner than invoke the Ordinance *per se*, many Chiefs hurriedly signed Bye-laws and speedily achieved the objects for which the Department had been fighting desperately for more than two decades. Within a year the area of constituted Reserves had more than doubled to 751 square miles. In addition there were a further 617 square miles demarcated and awaiting constitution. Eleven years later, in 1939, the permanent high forest estate was almost complete: 5,771 square miles of forest had been demarcated and protected by law. A little later Winston Churchill was crying for tools 'to finish the job'. We had the tools, the men and the forest, and when the exigencies of the war allowed us, we got on with our job. In 1923, L. A. King-Church had replaced McLeod who retired as Conservator of Forests; Burbridge and Gent too had gone and new names were appearing in the staff lists: 'Bertie' Moor, Gordon Greene, L. C. Rowney, Wills, Cox, Vigne, all arrived within the next couple of years, but at that time the European staff comprised the Conservator, eight Assistant Conservators and three Foresters. In addition there were two African Foresters and twenty-seven Forest Guards. In the Annual Report for 1924, the Conservator of Forests wrote:

' All the officers have worked well. The nature of the work, viz., the selection of areas for Reserves and demarcation of boundaries, has involved for most of the staff during the whole eighteen months' tour almost constant living alone under bush conditions either under canvas or in small native villages. Insufficiency of quarters has also prevented officers from enjoying that relaxation from the work which prevents them getting stale and leads to greater efficiency.'

He referred to an allowance made to officers in lieu of quarters, but inferred that this, though generous, was not what was needed. He concluded:

> 'Whereas it is considered that 20-25% of the forest zone should be maintained under forest, at the end of the period under review it is possible only to say that 2½% has been or will shortly be reserved. . . .'

Fifty years ago Ghana was a wild country, inhabited by a sparse population lacking a franchise, illiterate for the most part, indulging here and there in human sacrifice and worshipping blood and soil. No strenuous efforts appear to have been made to explain the purpose of the proposed forest bill. The people thought, and many still think, that reservation involved Government appropriation of the land. In the vernacular the Forest Reserves are still referred to as *Aban asase*—Government land. Yet the Ordinance itself made clear, as generations of foresters have emphasized, that reservation does not alter ownership: Section 18(1) of Cap. 157 reads:

> 'The ownership of land within a proposed Forest Reserve shall not be altered by its constitution as a Forest Reserve.'

The demarcation of a proposed Reserve is the culmination of a good deal of bush-work (in West Africa the forest, in all its forms, is 'the bush'. A man does not travel in the forest; he 'goes to bush') and sometimes, considerable and protracted argument. When Forest Ranger A. E. Ackwah with some trepidation marched at the head of his carriers along the road towards Begoro in 1937, to begin the demarcation of the proposed Dede Forest Reserve, two years had elapsed since the area had been inspected and a selection report submitted.

The Selection Report described the area, its approximate boundaries, ownership, and reasons for reservation:

> 'as a barrier Reserve to prevent the advance of dry savannah conditions and to protect the steep slopes within the scarp from erosion. It will prove of protective value to the large area of forest now being taken up for cocoa north and north-east of Begoro.'

The latter is the headquarters of the caretaker chief, the Ben-

kumhene (the Chief of the left wing. Benkum=left; Ohene=
Chief) about fifteen miles to the south. Ownership is vested in the
Paramount Stool of Akim Abuakwa whom the Benkumhene
serves. *It is anticipated,* prophesied the report, *that the Benkumhene will oppose constitution.* . . . The area lies atop of the scarp
with ground up to 1,400 feet, precipitous slopes, some with patches
of grass among the forest, and overlooking to the north the wide
Afram River, and beyond it the vast plains covered with savannah
forest, which take their name from the river.

The survey of the area could not have been easy, opposition
apart, for much of the boundaries cross precipitous slopes or follow
high and close-set contours. The Conservator of Forests (the late
R. C. Marshall) approved the selection and the Forests Ordinance
was then invoked to constitute the Reserve and afford it the protection provided by law. The landowner, Sir Nana Ofori Atta,
whose death six years later was to invoke some of the most barbaric
customs of the country, including human sacrifice, was officially
served with Notice that reservation was proposed. The bailiff, who
served the Notice swore that he did so before the District Commissioner, Kibi, received his mileage and service fees of 14s, and
on the 8 June 1937 the Acting Conservator of Forests (H. W. Moor)
officially wrote to the Provincial Forest Officer, Koforidua (C.
Vigne): 'Please expedite demarcation of the proposed (Dede)
Forest Reserve.'

Vigne's response was to request 'two blank field books for the
survey', which illustrates the parsimony which dogged our heels
and hedged our work in those days. That the Provincial Forest
Officer in charge of an area as large as Yorkshire should have to
ask his Head of Department for two 6d field books, reflected the
financial stringency imposed on the Department. Worse, there
were no field books at Accra, and the request had to be referred to
Kumasi, where I presume they were available. A little later when
I taught the Learner Forest Rangers, I experienced the greatest
difficulty in obtaining such vital items as drawing paper, pencils
and chalk for the blackboard.

Meanwhile the Benkumhene had submitted a petition to His
Excellency the Governor objecting to the proposal, supported by
a letter from the Omanhene. The latter was brief, whereas the
petition spread itself over five typewritten pages beginning:

To His Excellency Sir Arnold Wienholt Hodson, Knight Commander of the Most Distinguished Order of St Michael and St George etc etc.

In essence the petition maintained that the reasons which the Forestry Department had given for reservation were untenable and that the reasons *they* themselves gave *against* reservation were apposite i.e. they pleaded shortage of land for food farming. The Omanhene in his supporting letter made it clear that the feeling of his subjects 'had been considerably stirred-up'.

Before commenting on the petition, which had to circumnavigate the 'usual channels', the Provincial Commissioner Eastern Province (S. W. Saxton, who was to 'welcome' me to the Coast a year later), arranged that the District Commissioner, Kibi, and the PFO should inspect the proposed Reserve with representatives of Begoro 'as it is clear that the petitioners are very vague as to the extent of the area to be included'.

The Acting PFO (I. A. Beveridge) in company with the District Commissioner Kibi, with carriers, tents and full loads, carried out the inspection and reported at length on the 28 September 1937. Their inspection showed that a considerable amount of cocoa farming was being done all around the proposed Reserve on land sold by Begoro to strangers, mainly Krobos. Their plea that they were short of food farms was true only inasmuch as they had *sold* potential food farms for cocoa growing, an all too common practice. Representatives of Begoro, though requested to accompany the inspecting party, did not put in an appearance, a common enough occurrence and one that used to infuriate more placid officers than myself. Beveridge reported the presence of 'scouts' who were, presumably, keeping an eye on the inspecting party.

On the strength of Beveridge's report, the Commissioner Eastern Province sent Begoro's petition on the next leg of its journey to the Governor, addressing his own comments on the matter to the Hon. Colonial Secretary, the late Sir G. E. London). The CEP although *agreeing* with most of what Beveridge had said concluded his observations with this astonishing admission: 'I find myself still unable to support the view that . . . the creation of this Reserve is of vital importance to the Colony.'

The Conservator of Forests, in turn commenting on the petition, expressed his 'surprise' at this statement (which reminds us of the reaction of Mr Webster, the compiler of the famous dictionary, who was discovered by Mrs Webster kissing the maid. 'I'm surprised at you! ' she exclaimed. Imperturbably the great lexicographer disentangled himself and corrected her: 'It is I who am surprised, my dear; *you*, are astonished! ').

Captain Marshall, always mild-mannered, completed his minute by stating simply: 'This Reserve is necessary and I can find only one objection to it. It is not large enough.'

His Excellency backed the Conservator, and through the Colonial Secretary instructed the CEP 'to inform the Benkumhene and his Councillors that His Excellency is unable to grant their prayer. . . .' The CEP, however, was not quite done with and he kept the minute papers flowing by pointing out that in spite of considerable efforts to convince Begoro and his followers of the necessity for reservation they were firmly set against it. Further, that if demarcation was pressed 'care will have to be taken to safeguard against a breach of the peace'. H. E. nevertheless promptly issued an instruction that demarcation was to proceed forthwith. On receiving his demarcation orders Forest Ranger Ackwah promptly asked for, and was granted, police protection.

Demarcation was well under way when a petition from Sir Mate Kole, Konor of Manya Krobo, was sent to His Excellency requesting that demarcation be suspended pending an enquiry into the investment by his subjects to the tune of £15,000 in land purchases in the area. This was really big money in those days. On the advice of the CEP (A. Duncan-Johnstone) demarcation continued.

The work which had been attended by so much acrimony and threats was finally completed early in 1939 and the demarcation report was submitted to the Conservator in May of the same year. From the time of issue of the Governor's intention to constitute the Dede Forest Reserve in 1937, it was protected by Section 6 of the Forests Ordinance and offenders could be prosecuted under the Ordinance.

Constitution could always be made under Bye-laws, subject to certain conditions. Such Bye-laws were signed by Akim Abuakwa and Manya Krobo later in 1937, but owing to the land dispute between the two states, His Excellency declined to approve these Bye-laws. It was not until *July 1955* that a Reserve Settlement

Commissioner (C. H. Cooke) was appointed in accordance with Section 5 of the Ordinance.

During the course of the enquiry, which lasted, on and off, for two years, it was discovered that the original notice served by the bailiff in 1937 could not be produced as required by law. Finally, it was dug out of the National Archives and the enquiry was completed in March, 1957. During the ensuing six months' period in which appeals may be made, one, John Djabotey, appealed against the RSC's judgment. This appeal was ultimately thrown out and upon notification of this, I drafted an order for the constitution of the Dede Forest Reserve which was signed by the Minister of Agriculture and duly appeared in the Gazette. It had taken us twenty-two years to achieve. Others have taken longer, but few have involved such bickering.

Head Forester P. B. Cann-Sagoe, who gave thirty-five years of impeccable service to the Department, writing to the author after his retirement in 1958, gives an account of the difficulties which he, as a very junior Ranger, had to contend with in Ashanti during the early days of Reserve selection.

The country's forest policy in the main was very unpalatable. After several futile attempts the then Conservator responsible, the late N. C. McLeod, succeeded at last in appearing before that august body the 'Aborigines' Rights Protection Society' a body composed of Chiefs and intelligentsia and addressed them on the proposed forest policy in January, 1923. The address contained in a small pamphlet with red cover, the exact title of which I cannot recollect, although I helped with typescript.

The first Reserve to be selected and demarcated was the Mankrang Offin Forest Reserve in 1923 by Messrs Froude Burnett and J. D. McAinsh, ACFS in the teeth of very strong opposition. Threats of shooting and beating up of labourers were rife. In some cases Escort Police had to accompany these officers in their movements in the forest and elsewhere. The writer, the then first trained African to be stationed in Ashanti, had to face the music in 1926. Free hand fightings culminating in fighting with sticks with attendant threats of shooting were reported here and there. Incessant protest appeals were made to the then Kumasihene, Nana Prempeh I of revered memory. The Reserve was later abandoned for some reason and in 1927-28 the Tano Offin Reserve was selected and demarcated. In 1925 Kumasi Town Forest Reserve and the

Offin Headquarters came into being. In the former the village of Adiebeba was the bone of contention even to the very present time Threats of shooting and fighting were constant. The writer was at the scene up to 1928 when Mr Vigne took over for silvicultural purposes with other Foresters viz. Ackwah, Jackson and the late Andoh.

In 1927, threats of shooting and fighting especially at Prah River and Mramra on the Accra road in connection with the South Fomang Su Reserve. The writer and other African Foresters were involved.

From 1927, the writer faced threats of shooting especially at Ninting, Hwidiem, Jamase, Tabure and Mprim. Several arrests and prosecutions resulted.

Mr Froude Burnett, ACF, started demarcation (of the Pamu Berekum Reserve early in 1930) for about six weeks and left off, and never returned to the country. The writer completed the entire demarcation which took him six months. Threats of shooting and imprisonment (came) from outside, mainly the French. The arrest of the writer, his subsequent escape and continuous threats of shooting resulted in the abandoning of portion of the west boundary which was shifted about two miles inside the British side, the original west boundary being a portion of the International Frontier. The original name of Anglo-French Frontier Reserve was changed in consequence. In those days communication was not as easy as it is today. Letters (by bearer) took longer time to reach their destinations. When it was considered necessary to proceed with demarcation of this Reserve, the Gold Coast Government communicated with the French authorities intimating their intention. Demarcation was commenced long before the information reached the French District Commandant in that area. On hitting the frontier I pitched my tent. A French patrol made up of five men including a white officer arrived, entered my tent and demanded my authority to camp there. On failing to produce one I was escorted to an outpost about five miles away and questioned at length and detained. As I could not speak French an old British discharged soldier at that time in French service acted as interpreter. On my stating that I was an assistant to a European Officer in charge of the operation it was decided to have me detained until the arrival of the said Officer. If after a week the said officer had not arrived I would be taken to Bontuku for trial. That was on the 10 December, 1930. On the 12th I provided a large bottle of French gin I had secured and the old war veteran helped himself very well and became very drunk as a result. I took the advantage and stealthily, at the dead of night in clear moonlight, accompanied by my Forest Guard and Headman escaped by way of my cut line until a village called Brofuyedru where the bulk of my labourers were was reached after about four hours' walk. Message was sent to Captain Greene, then Acting PFO, about the experience, who came out and ordered alteration of the original boundary to avoid any reprisal by the French.

No protest demonstration was made in respect of the Bosumkese Forest Reserve. The threats were supernatural. (Bosumkese means 'Big Spirit'.) Ghost haunt made life miserable. I had to change a camping place when I was haunted by some spirits which made an unusual noise culminating in the marching of some soldiers. Mr. Cox, ACF, then in charge of Sunyani, came out on a survey check and arrived at my camping place about 3.30 p.m. on a Friday. He delivered a telegram received from my wife reporting the death of my second son. After reporting my own experiences I left for Kumasi on six days casual leave for the funeral. He proceeded to my former camping place but could not sleep. On meeting him at Sunyani he reported how he shouted for the labourers to come to his aid during the night. He heard the marching of a great army of men with shouting and the giving of commands, identical to my experience. He left for Sunyani the next day very frightened. This camp site which was the abandoned site of the old Dormaa town called Bampredasi was finally excluded from the Reserve.

FARM AND FOREST

Having secured his forest estate, the forester must manage it. In the high forest zone of Ghana, where there are two kinds of forest estate, management had to be varied to suit each one. Outside the permanent forest estate (the Forest Reserves) lay the greater area of unreserved forest. The former has been gradually built up to its present peak of about twenty per cent of the high forest zone. No further reservation is planned. Of the unreserved forest, which at the beginning of the century covered most of the zone and was scarcely touched by man except for minutely small food farms, little now remains. This forest has gone; it has been hacked and burned to make room for cocoa. Now, except for a few concession areas in the west, as yet inviolate, all that remains is a honeycomb of farm and forest, the latter exploitable only at the risk of expensive damage to cocoa.

Forestry is properly the handmaiden of agriculture and the most economical use of the soils of Ghana is to plant paying agricultural crops. Cocoa is the most paying crop, a perennial one, and is likely to remain so for some time. The danger of a one-crop economy, upon which Ghana at the moment is precariously balanced, is apparent, even to the Government. Practically every voter, whether he is a civil servant, lorry driver, politician, fisherman or trader, is also a farmer; his wife and children also probably have some interest in the land. Until the farmer is shown a crop that is as simple to grow and tend, and is as profitable, as cocoa, he will continue to grow cocoa. There is no one as conservative as a farmer, unless it be a timber man: launching a new wood on the world's markets is a heart-breaking task.

That all soils in Ghana are not equally suited to the growth of cocoa is a fact which has not yet been properly digested. Thousands of acres of cocoa have perished because of this fact. The dictum always has been that where the forest is, cocoa will thrive. But first you must knock down the forest and burn it. The legend of the great fertility of tropical forest soils still persists. The cold fact that such soils are fertile only while under the forest that created them, is not known to one farmer in a thousand. Therein lies one of the main reasons for the failure of the cocoa industry to expand: production has remained almost static for thirty years and may now be on its way down to a slump which could impoverish Ghana, in spite of the record 1960 crop.

Man is a puny creature and of all the animals one of the least suited to life in the forest. But even man when armed with a cutlass and a firebrand can easily destroy that which has existed for countless centuries. He has done so with ever-increasing pace for half a century. He would have done it in far less time but for one factor: access. Agriculture spread like an epidemic rash from the towns and villages. Food was the primary concern: the people had to eat. Down came the forest around the population centres and as shifting cultivation was practised too diligently by too many people, scrub-land now marks much of the suburbs. People had to travel farther and farther to make and tend their farms, commuting on foot. Even today roads cannot tap more than a minute fraction of the farms that exist.

The expansion of the cocoa-growing industry was limited by the difficulty of access, of getting into the untouched forest and of getting the cocoa out. To expedite this development roads were necessary. The farmer and his community represented by the Native, now the Local, Authorities, could not afford to build all the roads needed to tap the vast cocoa potential. The sudden and colossal expansion of the timber industry in the postwar years, which in a single decade increased the exports of logs from 4 million cubic feet in 1946 to 15½ million in 1956, and sawn timber from ¼ million to 7¾ million cubic feet and raised the total production of sawn timber from 7¼ million to 44 million cubic feet, resulted, indirectly, in the complete destruction of some 5,000 square miles of forest. This resulted also in a loss to the country in the form of log exports alone of some £200 million and to the Stools and Local councils of some £5 million. The former would have paid for the First Development Plan and the latter would have provided much-needed schools, sanitation and roads to many areas suffering from their lack.

The timber trade, however, was only indirectly responsible for this.

New hauling roads spread like the roots of a tree, probing almost every part of the exploitable forest. The farmers raced in, even as the road traces were being cut, and began the destruction of the forest. Even in Concession areas, protected by legally validated leases which often cost the holders many thousands of pounds in bribes and consideration money, much weary negotiation and cases of gin, even in these areas, the law offered no protection against the farmer who, with the landowner's consent, could destroy as much of the forest as he and his family and hired labour could manage. The unfortunate Concessionaire could not fell and haul out his logs until his roads were made, and while he was spending £1,000 a mile on this work, the farmer was ahead of him burning and felling all the trees he wanted to make way for his cocoa seedlings. When the cocoa had matured and produced its first crop of beans, these would be hauled over the timber Concessionaire's roads as he pleased.

The small timber man with a lorry or two, perhaps an old

tractor, lived a very much hand-to-mouth existence. This does not imply that properly run it could not be an exceedingly profitable business. There is still money in wood, though the easy boom years have gone, and the small man, black or white, could if he tried, build up a prosperous business. The late George Grant starting from nothing earned and spent several fortunes in his life time, and a score of men of narrower vision are today comparatively wealthy men without ever having had to acquire capital.

It is maintained by the disgruntled that the pickings always went to the European. Usually they did, but rarely without considerable hard work and costly investment. R. T. Briscoe made himself a millionaire in little more than a decade, starting from nothing: no capital, no experience. Umiker and Fluekiger, that improbable sounding combination, who knew not balk from bark, or an inserted tooth from a false one when they began, sold out for a reputed quarter-of-a-million within a decade. They acquired some of the richest concessions in West Africa, built themselves a sawmill out of bits and pieces and with only their native shrewdness and a capacity for hard work, made for themselves a great name in the cut-throat competition which is the timber trade.

The little man in timber rarely bothers about the expensive and protracted business of obtaining a validated Concession, which is the only way in which timber rights may be protected (except against the farmer) by the law. He may rue this omission later, but usually he is content to obtain a felling agreement from a Chief which is not worth the paper on which it is printed. To have any validity an agreement must pass through the tortuous channels prescribed by the Concessions Ordinance. This may take years and swallow up a lot of money. The simple felling agreement allows a certain number of trees to be felled in a specified area, which may, or may not, have specific boundaries, at certain specified royalty rates. Consideration money, not mentioned, but always exacted, and a case or two of gin, are prerequisites. An identical agreement can be, and sometimes is, concluded with another contractor. This naturally often leads to bitter acrimony and noisy wrangling during which a third contractor may enter the contest and fell and remove his logs before the protagonists realize what is happening. There is no legal redress. The felling agreement has no legal status. Meanwhile the landowner sits back with a happy sigh, content with three lots of fees which are by then earning interest in the local post office savings bank. The fact that this money belongs not to the landowner, but to the Stool concerned and ought to pass through the Local Authority acounts for proper distribution, does not lie heavily on his conscience.

The expatriate investor cannot afford such slipshod business. He is far from home, has no local 'pull' and is expected to pay a premium price for what he wants. He is usually working on a far larger scale than his African counterpart, using expensive machinery and employing, often, large numbers of Africans. He must secure his investment and the only means available is the Concessions Ordinance, a poor instrument, but the only one. The selling of land between Africans is a new thing and was unknown until this century. Land was something you did not sell; it was not 'done'; 'sell' your wife and daughters if you liked, your slaves if you had any, but land was your connection with the past, your communion with the future. Next to blood, kith and kin, it was, and is still largely, the most important thing in an African's life. Without land you were nothing and had nothing to hand on to your descendants.

Land has never been sold to the white man. He may lease it for a consideration and a rental and by royalty payments. The negotiation of timber concessions, especially in later years as valuable trees became more scarce and less accessible, sometimes involved considerable acrimony, double dealing and threats of violence, even among Europeans. Some firms would go almost to any length, tell any lie and give monstrous bribes, to secure particularly valuable leases.

Considering the importance of land to the Ghanaian, it is astonishing that he did so little in the past to define and mark its boundaries. The latter often followed streams, paths and thin-cut lines to trees or even bottles stuck in the ground. Streams change courses, a cut line is invisible after a few months, and no path is static. Trees die and rot and bottles disappear. It is not then strange that many boundaries are hotly disputed. Owners will litigate to their last penny and beyond to fight a land case. They will squander money on appeal after appeal right up to the Privy Council, even though they, and their legal advisers know that their chances are negligible. Such recourse to the law is largely a matter of 'face'; it is also what the Pools are in England (and fast becoming in Ghana too), a gamble.

Where neither side can point to a sensible boundary, the legal wrangling goes senselessly on profiting no one but their lawyers and solicitors. The Government is helping here and a Land Boundary Commission is now at work, but with no hope of covering the whole of Ghana before the end of this century. Revenue which should accrue from such disputed lands is unearned, the trees stand, grow old, fall and rot, and not a penny comes into the Stool chest; the drains continue to stink and the people suffer the pain and sickness of hookworm and bilharzia, because there is no piped water, because there is no revenue.

Having finally secured his 'number'—the number of the Certificate of Validation—some years after he first filed a court application for a concession, and 'light' by some thousands of pounds, the Concessionaire might then logically expect that his trees, those for which he has paid considerably in time, money and health, would be his for the taking. How naïve he would be! Every Certificate of Validation contains a clause which specifies that the rights and interests of farmers must be protected. 'Farmer' means anyone who wants to make a farm. The Concessions Ordinance states : *No Concession shall be certified as valid unless the Court is satisfied that the customary rights of Natives are reasonably protected in respect of cultivation.* (Cap. 136, Sec. 13 (6).) This means that any Ghanaian may destroy as much forest as he wishes, anywhere, in advance of exploitation if need be. The Concession holder can do nothing.

The value of this loss of timber rights thus inflicted on Concessionaires cannot accurately be determined. The uncontrolled farming which the Concessions Ordinance permitted until 1959, when some control of farming was given to Government, resulted in millions of acres of good forest—many millions of valuable trees—being destroyed. Royalties vary from place to place and from species to species and from time to time: Odum (Iroko) tops the list at £8-£12 per tree, a 'new' species now in great demand in the furniture trade, *Afrormosia*, is a good second; mahogany comes next at £4-£6 per tree, and other species vary considerably down to 15s for those for which there is little demand. The loss of royalties to the people through the Local Councils must have amounted to millions of pounds, while Ghana itself was deprived, senselessly, of a natural asset that can never be replaced. It would have been a simple matter to legislate so that the 'customary rights of natives' were allowed *after* exploitation. The new Timber Lands Protection Bill (1959) achieves this. It should have achieved it a generation earlier and would have done so if the Department of Forestry had been allowed to perform its proper function as Forestry advisers to the Government. It would have enabled Stools and Local Councils to advance the level of rural economy considerably beyond the often pitiful stages of present-day achievement.

This loss, estimated in millions of pounds, which the Concessionaires have suffered in the past two decades, will oblige the great expatriate firms to leave Ghana much earlier than they otherwise would have done. Some will cut their losses and seek business elsewhere even before their present concessions have been worked out. The large modern sawmills which until recently were working overtime will close down; a valuable flourishing industry must inevitably grind slowly into low gear, causing unemployment of men skilled in the business of sawing and logging and a slump in the value of exports of wood.

A generation ago, a Timber Lands Protection Bill would by now have brought prosperity, modern drainage, sanitation, piped water, i.e. a level of human comfort often dreamed of, but rarely acquired in West Africa, to many towns and villages. It would have ensured a continuity in the timber trade without which industrial success must founder. Control of farming would have allowed the management of concession areas to ensure some sort of sustained yield. This would have tided over the difficult and dangerous period between now and the day, some forty years hence, when the permanent forest estate, by its present development and improvement, can meet all the country's demands for wood. A degree of permanence could have been assured to all those with investments in the trade which would have preserved their roots and maintained the considerable prosperity which the country's second most valuable industry provides.

But the Government, fearful of its prestige among the people, farmers all, with its eye on political continuity, let the farmer have his way. The consequences of this political cowardice will not be obvious for a decade or two; but that the consequences will be painful, I have no doubt. At the time of writing, Ghana's timber production is probably at or near its peak and within the next decade, as the unreserved forest disappears completely, it is almost certain that the value of timber exports will fall catastrophically.

At present only about one-eighth of Ghana's timber is cut on a sustained yield basis i.e. is cut in the Forest Reserves. The remainder is cut wherever and whenever it is found. Before the Timber Lands Protection Bill came into force, in 1959, the rate of cutting outside the Reserves was estimated to be such as to exhaust all major sources of supply within ten to fifteen years. Many sawmills were resigned to closing down within this period.

The Bill will control farming to some extent and thus extend the productive period of the unreserved forest a little longer. The recession will be held off; it cannot be stopped. Control has come too late. Production on a sustained yield basis, which means production in *perpetuity*, from the Forest Reserves has not yet reached its peak. Five years ago it was less than 1 million cubic feet per annum; in 1958 it was nearly 7 million and is expected to double this figure in two years. By the end of the century it is expected to meet all the foreseeable demands made on it by the timber industry.

Growth in the tropical forest, though faster than in temperate zones, is still much slower than it can be made to be. The trees are so thick and the competition for water and light so fierce and sustained, that much of the trees' energies are directed towards mere survival. The means to accelerate the pace of growth by introducing more light and eliminating unwanted species are now being applied to the permanent forest estate on an ever-increasing scale. The numbers of species wanted by the world's markets represent a small proportion of the numbers growing in the forest and the poisoning of useless species will accelerate the pace of growth of the remainder and will also allow more of the remainder to grow.

The full effect of these silvicultural measures cannot be felt in less than forty years; consequently, as the extent of the unreserved forest gradually diminishes to nothing, there will be a hiatus whose effects must be serious. It need not have happened.

The Concessions Ordinance was designed primarily to protect the Gold Mining industry: gradually it was modified to give protection to those engaged in the Timber Industry: the landowners, the farmers, even those unborn, and the Concessionaire himself. That it failed was due to the obtuseness of the Government. The Ordinance provided wide controlling powers for the Chief Conservator of Forests. As adviser in Forestry to the Government, he was in a position to plan the orderly exploitation of the forest in Concessions. No Concessionaire could, legally, exploit his timber without first seeking the 'conditions, restrictions, limitations and directions' which the Chief Conservator was empowered to impose.

Before such control could be formulated, the area had to be inspected, reported on and a scheme of management drawn up with which the Concessionaire must comply. The purpose was to conserve the country's timber as long as possible without unduly impeding exploitation by the numerous timber firms which invaded the timber field just after the second world war.

The Forestry Department divided concession areas into two groups: those in which the forest was immediately threatened by farming, and those where farming was unlikely to threaten the forest for some years. In the former there was no management and the exploiters were given *carte blanche*, even exhorted, to fell and to salvage everything they could as fast as they could, and they were excused from compliance with the Trees and Timber (Control of Cutting) Regulations which safeguarded immature trees. In the latter, plans were prepared based on enumeration surveys (counts) done by the operators and checked by the Department, and proper extraction routes aligned and a scheme of orderly cutting prescribed. Immature trees were protected. The 'conditions, restrictions, limitations and directions' were being imposed and were not liked.

At this time (c. 1946) the problems of management of the permanent forest estate were just beginning to make themselves felt and the District Forest Officer, who until then had not been overburdened with paper work, suddenly found himself in the position of a man riding two horses moving in opposite directions. We have never had enough staff, particularly field staff, and have always had to fight to increase the cadre, in spite of the fact that our work has continuously intensified and increased. From this time on we had to fight harder than ever.

On the one hand there were inspections and checks and concession reports and plans to be drawn up, and more inspections and checks to see that the plans were being followed. On the other hand similar, but more precise, plans for the Forest Reserves had to be written and put into effect. The District Forest Officer had no one to advise him in the compilation of his plans; no one had ever written an intensive Working Plan for the forests of Ghana and most ideas were tenuous and had never been tested in the field.

Before catastrophe hit us we were reprieved by the sudden realization that the farmers were destroying the forest far faster than we had estimated.

The total area of unreserved forest was estimated at 11,000 square miles in 1946. We considered that this represented at least forty years of exploitation, during which time the Department would be able to put its management plans into operation throughout the permanent forest estate and so contrive to boost the sustained yield so that when the unreserved forest was utterly destroyed sufficient timber could be obtained from the Forest Reserves to meet all the trade's demands. In 1952 and 1953, however, detailed surveys of areas in which cocoa had been planted, supplemented by our own surveys, revealed the unpalatable fact that farming had been taking place at a far greater pace than we had believed possible. The area of the unprotected forest was then computed to be little greater than that of the protected forest, viz., about 6,000 square miles. The rate of destruction by farming was approaching 1,000 square miles (640,000 acres) a year. Had this been maintained, the unprotected forest would already have gone and the second most valuable export trade in Ghana would now be occupying a much more lowly place.

Overboard went our ideas of planned and organized management in the Concessions. The Concessions Ordinance was biting its own tail with a vengeance. On the one hand it prescribed powers for the Chief Conservator to control felling; on the other, its insistence on the rights of natives nullified those powers. To the relief of the Concessionaires, control was relaxed. It now became a race between them and the farmers, a race which is still proceeding, and one in which there will be no winners.

Exports at this stage (1952-3) were in the region of 9 million cubic feet of logs and lumber. They were to rocket to 55 million cubic feet by 1958, and though this figure might be sustained, even increased slightly, for a short time, nothing is more certain than a sharp recession.

The tragedy of West African forestry is the fantastic waste attending the multiple operations of felling and extraction, and all too often the milling itself. Before the last war, the export market was confined almost entirely to mahogany and pseudo-mahogany (the cedars, some of which have a mahogany-like appearance and could be reckoned to fool all but the most critical buyers in those days). The accent on mahogany continued until well after the war when its available volume began steadily to decline. So great had been the demand for this wood, to the exclusion of all others, that accessible stocks began to run out and since then its export volume has declined.

Fortunately for the local trade, central Europe began to show a lively interest in a relatively new wood, a soft, light, easily worked and fairly stable wood, that was available in vast quantities, known as Wawa (the trade name is Obeche). In 1946 only a few thousand cubic feet were exported; by 1958 exports had shot up to more than 13 million cubic feet, more than half the total volume of logs exported in that year.

Apart from this, and *Afrormosia*, a worthy substitute for teak, unfortunately restricted to a narrow belt of forest in north-west Ashanti, the market was scarcely less conservative than it had been twenty years before.

The common species of the forest (apart from Wawa) such as Dahoma (*Piptadeniastrum*) and Esa (*Celtis*), which between them often comprise half the standing volume of the forest, remain untouched. The trade cannot find a use for them. When it *has* to find a use for them I have little doubt that it will do so. Careless and casual methods of felling and logging contribute to the waste of good wood. Trees are badly felled and split; logs are cross-cut in the wrong places; sometimes the wrong species are cut. So they lie in the forest, unwanted. Failure to pay labour promptly has always been a problem among the numerous 'small men' who lack capi-

Above: Big wood: see men at top right. *Bottom left:* How they used to do it: skidding a log over the 'corduroy'. *Bottom right:* Felling a mahogany.

Above: A forest ranger's camp in the Bobiri forest reserve. *Below:* The bush.

tal. Often, before they can pay their 'boys' they must sell their logs, and they cannot always sell their logs until the 'boys' will move them, which they will not do until they are paid.

So the logs lie; the beetles bore their way in: fungi collaborate and by the time funds are again available (sometimes they never are) the logs are useless or command such low prices that the timber man finds himself still in debt. Very likely the landowner has been kept waiting for the price of the trees. If the logs are not sold profitably, he will wait, probably, forever, thereby encouraging him to double-deal the next seekers after a felling agreement.

Before the war sawmill production was negligible and confined almost entirely to mahogany. A mill requires capital, machinery, trained personnel. In those days local demand was slight: the pit-sawyer met most of the internal demand. Then, the soft-wood milling industry of Europe could meet all Europe's demands. Burdened with the cost of the long sea haul, lumber from Ghana was priced out of the European market.

As West African woods gradually became known on the world's markets, mainly in log form, for logging needs a minimum of capital, machinery and trained men, as war-shattered Europe fought its way back to its knees, and as the iron curtain sequestered east and west, there was room for more lumber. On the coast of Ghana, but mainly up-country in the forest itself, new mills mushroomed and from almost nothing, the export lumber trade blossomed so that in the first decade after the war exports rose from 200,000 cubic feet, mainly mahogany, to 6½ million cubic feet of a dozen species. By 1958, exports had risen by another forty per cent and were valued at £4¾ million.

As the price of cocoa (5s a load in 1939) doubled, doubled again, and again doubled, the purchasing power of the people rose; development, both private and Government-sponsored, helped the sawmilling industry along. Internal consumption of mill-sawn wood in 1946 was practically nothing; but 1957 nearly 3½ million cubic feet were being used annually. In 1958 this dropped slightly, for the first year since 1945. Is this significant? Has the peak been reached? The next few years will tell us.

We believe we have solved the major problems of silviculture. We believe we can grow the valuable wanted trees more quickly than they have previously grown, and in greater numbers. Our major problem is now one of utilization. The Utilization Branch of the Division is now concentrating on the employment of 'new' species. At the moment, 'new' woods from the Old World are seemingly unwanted outside Africa. As Africa gains more independence, as her internal economy expands, she will require, as Ghana is requiring, ever-increasing quantities of wood for development. Her forests can supply them, new woods and old.

CHAPTER FIVE

Guarding the Forest Reserves

A FOREST RESERVE, if it is not too large, constitutes a single beat under the charge of a Forest Guard. His duties are to ensure that the demarcated boundaries (both the external and the internal ones marking all farms, research areas, fetish groves, camps and, occasionally, villages) are kept clean, that the cement pillars placed at half-mile intervals and at major changes of direction are preserved. Elephant dislike white and they sometimes remove cement pillars with a twist of their trunks and tread them deeply into the ground with their massive feet. Caterpillar tractors occasionally smash them, floods sometimes undermine them and unscrupulous farmers dig them up and replant them elsewhere. A Forest Guard can arrest suspected offenders against the Forest Laws and must patrol his beat systematically to see that the local population are not carving themselves chunks of Reserve land and altering boundaries to suit themselves.

Until recently the Forest Guard divided his time between cleaning and patrolling. The former is a job which no machine yet devised can perform economically, and chemical methods now being tried seem too expensive. The traditional cutlass or machete wielded by a strong right arm cleans some 17,000 miles of Reserve boundary each year. Each boundary, according to a written schedule, is cleaned twice annually.

So long as this work is achieved it is little matter whether the Forest Guard himself does it or engages a labourer to do it. Many senior Forest Guards on distant beats where inspections by the Forest Ranger are few and far between take their ease in this way, spending most of the month in leisurely patrolling interspersed with hunting and trapping. At the monthly pay-out the Forest Guard reports his cleaning schedule as completed for the month. If he has neglected to check that his labourer has in fact *cleaned* the beat, he can blame only himself if a subsequent inspection reveals that part of the line to be overgrown, and that the labourer did not honour his part of the bargain. Submission of a false report of this nature is not uncommon and usually means, in addition to the money lost to the defecting labourer, a lost increment.

In remote Reserves such as the Bia Tano and the Banda Hills, where there are few accessible villages and none within the Reserves, the Forest Guards lead lonely, arduous and sometimes dangerous lives, requiring considerable mental fortitude and physical stamina. Men of the north inured to hardship and want are almost exclusively recruited for this job. The coast boys, even the Ashantis famed for their prowess in war, have no stomach for this job, and who can blame them? Even the Bazabarimas, Moshies, Fulanis and Grunshis from the north do not always relish it. In the days when a Forest Guard's pay was £42 a year, I had several tough carriers who cheerfully carried a 60 lb load all day for a shilling a day, for as many days as one wished to employ them, but who would not take appointments as Forest Guards because of their fear of the bush.

Musa Moshie was one of these carriers who desperately wanted to become a Guard but whom I steadfastly refused appointment until he overcame his terror of the forest. In company, the carriers did not mind the nights in the bush; a solitary life was another matter. It was not only the beasts of the forest that worried them but the 'spirits' and the 'little people' who could destroy a man far more easily than the fangs of a cobra. For years Musa was the headman of my party of carriers, not that he was a particularly good headman, for he was by his own admission a timorous soul, but he alone spoke pidgin English and relieved me of the labour of translating my wishes into indifferent Twi or abominable Hausa. It was also comforting to have someone with whom to converse apart from one's boy. Kodjo-the-cook was a taciturn individual not given to light banter. Musa, on the other hand, could talk the hind leg off a donkey and would happily translate the most lascivious of the carriers' songs with which they lightened their burdens in the early morning (later in the day they were too tired).

Every three months or so Musa presented himself in his best cloth at my office and resumed his nagging demands to make him a Forest Guard. 'You fear too much, Musa,' I told him. Always his response was, 'I no fear so much, sah,' and he would go away.

Little by little Musa conquered his fear, or controlled it, until one day he appeared and instead of the well worn formula he blurted out 'Sah, I tink I no fear at all' with great emphasis on the last word. I promptly posted him, on probation, to the furthermost Reserve in the District, the North Bandai Hills, a long rectangle of forest and scrub protruding into the Afram Plains. It was a new Reserve, its boundaries yet uncleared. Two weeks later I ended up in the same place and set out to find if probationer Forest Guard Musa Moshie had stayed put, or whether his fears had proved too much for him. We followed the boundary which appeared freshly cut till distantly we heard the rhythmic sound of a cutlass being wielded. It was a beaming, confident Musa Moshie whom we met. He is still a Forest Guard now in northern Ghana.

With the evolution of the Division from a collection of bush-whackers to the function for which the senior officers were trained, the duties of Forest Guards were also modified. The exploitation of the permanent forest estate involves constant checking of the trees felled. An annual coupe (felling area) might extend over several square miles and the task of finding, checking and recording each felled tree is no light one. Not only did we require Forest Guards, but literate Forest Guards. To fill the newly-created grade of Technical Forest Guard we had to have men who 'savvy book', who could read and write sufficiently well to check numbers, record them and make brief written reports. These men, although they would receive no more pay than the purely protective Guards, were relieved of the duties of cleaning boundaries and were also eligible for promotion to the highest rank of Senior Forest Guard.

A Forest Guard is appointed as a Learner whether from the labourers' ranks or from selected ex-servicemen or schoolboys and serves a probationary period of three years. Promotion to Forest Guard is practically automatic. The highest grade of Senior Forest Guard, which is a pensionable post, is attainable only by Technical Forest Guards and those few Forest Guards (Protective) who achieve a minimum of twenty years' exemplary service.

The Forest Guards and the labourers from whose ranks many

are recruited constitute a remarkable body of men possessing qualities which few of us can boast. Most are illiterate, rarely see civilization, spend much of their time alone in the forest with a palm frond for a roof at night, yet are spanking smart when they turn up for payout at Range Headquarters each month. The dark green fez with its brass bugle badge and jaunty black tassel dangling over one eye, may not be the most sensible headgear for the forest, but it is impressive. The khaki shirt with its thick shoulder patch—doubtless a relic of the Army—khaki shorts 'pressed' in the Army fashion with soap, water and a scrubbing brush into knife-edged creases, khaki puttees and mirror-bright boots, and a broad leather belt embellished with a true guardsman's patent leather 'skin' compounded of much spit, polish and elbow grease, lose nothing in comparison with a Royal Marine's review order.

Some splendid characters grew up in the service. Paul Ampofo, long since retired, ruled the North Fomang Su Reserve for many years. Villagers would complain bitterly to me that 'Mr Paul' quite openly usurped my position and as far as the forest was concerned he behaved with more arrogance than their own chief. This I could well believe. Whenever I saw Paul, I felt as though I should pull back my shoulders and stand to attention. He was an ex-soldier with a precise soldierly bearing and manner, a uniform that would have pleased an adjutant of Marines, and a salute that would have sent a Coldstreamer back to his barracks to practice. He wore, not the regulation rough khaki puttees, but the soft, calf-shaping puttees by Fox, tied so that each overlap was *exactly* equal to the previous one and the pale tapes lay flat and even and with hardly a suggestion of tuck-in. His brass fez badge and shoulder title bars glowed with all the fire which much-used brass can summon. His English was correct and precise. There was scarcely a stick lifted, or a snail captured without his knowing of it and swooping on the offender with a swiftness and fury which suggested he was in league with the 'little people', notwithstanding that the North Fomang Su measures eight miles by four miles and is one of the wettest areas it was ever my misfortune to wade through. Fines for such offences were invariably higher than anywhere else in the District, eloquent testimony to Paul's efficiency in putting his cases to the courts.

So ruthless was he in his pursuit of the wrong-doer that for years there was practically no worth-while offence in his beat. Things came to such a pitch that I was more than once petitioned by villagers for permission to exercise their age-old rights. There was some suggestion that Paul accepted bribes, but once when a group of villagers came to see me on this matter and I insisted on calling Forest Guard Paul to hear their accusations they hastily dropped them and lit out of the office as fast as they decently could.

I never caught out old Paul, though after his retirement a decade ago, there was evidence that he had not been above a little surreptitious dealing in forest produce. Immediately following his retirement, the North Fomang Su once again registered prominently on the Forest Offences sheet.

There were some Forest Guards who could not resist the bottle or the calabash of palm wine. The tapping of the oil palm for the fizzy wine is carried out throughout the forest zone; elsewhere the Fan Palm is so treated. One of the Forest Guard's 'perks' is reckoned to be a portion of the tappers' yield. Who can blame the hardworking invariably thirsty and lonely Guard from seeking such gentle solace? Occasionally the 'perk' was not enough and there have been Forest Guards who have indulged in a little gratuitous tapping themselves, often with unpleasant results.

Many Guards are skilled trappers and hunters and usually carry a gun, either a cheap 12-bore or an even cheaper 'gas-pipe' gun, and exercise their skills to great degree. There is no law against hunting in a Forest Reserve (except in a few which are also Game Sanctuaries) but as many people still consider the Reserves to be *Aban Asase* (Government Land) they do not tempt providence and stay away. The sight of a Forest Guard will usually scare quite innocently-minded people and he fosters the illusion that his Reserve is sacrosanct and thereby not only preserves for himself a constant harvest of game, but also preserves a fauna which in many localities is being rapidly shot out of existence. Because hunting, to be successful, must be undertaken at night with the aid of an acetylene hunting lamp (because game is too sparse and too wary during the day) some Forest Guards tend to burn the candle at both ends to the ultimate detriment of their Beat duties. For sheer labour, line-cleaning with a cutlass is hard to beat. Night-hunting comes very close.

I thought I had become inured to the vague threats of the forest at night, its sudden scurries, the endless sibilance of uncountable leaves moving, of uncountable unseen creatures among and beneath the carpet of leaves, the sudden explosions of branches falling, of leopard coughing and the almost constant scream of the *Hyrax*. Years of tent life had made the forest a second home; I should have been uneasy were its sounds to cease. But I knew the forest at night from the comfort of a camp chair and camp bed. Until I walked the forest at night it had seemed a static thing; when I went night hunting the whole environment seemed to move; trees waved their branches, climbers actually writhed serpent-like. My first experience was almost a nightmare. We fumbled our way along a twisting hunter's trail, hardly visible in daylight let alone in complete darkness, guided only by a thin pencil of light from the accompanying hunter's acetylene headlamp. It seemed an endless agony of time as we shuffled and stumbled through the living forest. It is fortunate that we did not meet those other hunters, the driver ants. Being eyeless they need no light to find their prey. They spread out in their hundreds of thousands searching every millimetre of ground, every leaf, twig and branch. Few living creatures escape them; they are flushed and devoured alive. The lordly elephant, the deadly mamba, man himself is doomed unless by violent effort he escapes.

We had several false alarms, when the little column of men suddenly stopped and stood and listened. There was a sudden noisy movement of what sounded like large antelope which resolved themselves into moving leaves animated by a bush baby when the hunter turned up his lamp. Once we caught the twin glowing orbs of a pair of Pottos, matching almost the light from the hunter's lamp. Once the green eyes of a cat flickered from above and were gone; once, distantly, a noise like thunder betokened a falling tree. Periodically baboon barked with dog-like voices.

As I wished over and over again that I was in my bed (we had been on our feet most of the day), the hunter stopped. I stopped; the Ranger behind me stopped and the Forest Guard in the rear, stopped. It was the drill we had practised before. I could hear nothing unusual, could see nothing but the wan pencil of light and the dark moving shadows of trees all around us. It was damp now and the sweat lay cold upon me when suddenly the hunter moved, the lamp hissed and threw its bright beam forwards and downwards. I saw the large blue-green eyes of an animal transfixed by the light, saw its almost white body caught in the beam, heard the violent crash of the gun. The shock of the explosion doused the hunter's lamp and for a few moments we stood in absolute darkness. When the lamp had been relit we discovered our victim to be a fine, plump Maxwell's duiker. The hunter, Ranger and Guard were jubilant and were full of loud cheerful banter as we made our tortuous way back to camp. After hours of painful repression and enforced silence they let themselves go and made the welkin ring. The warm corpse of the duiker dripped its last blood on the shoulders of the hunter as he bore it triumphantly homewards.

The main role of the Forest Guard is to preserve the permanent forest estate. The Forest Ranger must manage that estate.

There is a lack of a tradition of learning in the majority of Ghanaian families; very often the boy is of the first entirely literate generation of his family and this seems to have resulted in parrot learning. The phenomenon exists in other countries where there is no long history of literacy. I recall that an Indian student who was doing his final chemistry with me at Cardiff, attempted the complete memorization of our organic chemistry textbook. That he failed is not surprising when one considers that the book held some 500 closely-printed pages.

So it is with many young Ghanaians. They study by parrot-like memorization rather than by understanding. Consequently when we sought suitable secondary schoolboys for training as Forest Rangers, we discovered to our astonishment that even those with passes in the General Certificate of Education often came fearful croppers in the entrance examination to the Forestry Learners' Training School, the standard of which is not, purposely, high.

The temptation to memorize without understanding is very strong and understandable in the circumstances. The result is to yield large numbers of well qualified young men most of whom find it difficult to reason competently, to observe dispassionately and to draw logical conclusions from their observations. For this reason we post the Learner Forest Ranger to the field for six

E*

months to allow him to get the feel of the forest and to gain a little practical understanding of what forestry means. We insist on this bush apprenticeship for another and no less vital reason : to weed out the ' white collar ' types.

Since literacy began in West Africa not much more than a century ago, the aim of the average boy who ' savvy book' is to obtain a ' white collar ' job, to become a clerk at least. The most influential families, those that can afford to send their children abroad for their education, or at least to the local University, have produced many eminent lawyers, a profession admirably suited to the West African's histrionic powers, and doctors. Though primarily agricultural, depending on the soil for prosperity, few of these families have put their sons on to the land as agricultural officers, or engineers, or foresters. Respectability is a fetish in Ghana no less than in Britain and the average boy would sooner be an ill-paid clerk in an office than what he contemptuously calls a ' bush man ', even though the latter is paid more. Fortunately for Ghana it is a trend that is gradually changing; the Government to their credit is extolling the ' dignity of labour ' and pictures of Cabinet Ministers ostensibly digging drains are aimed at encouraging the youth to work with their hands as well as with their heads. How much more virile Ghana's economy would be if all the Bannerman's, Quists, Asafu-Adgye's and Manyo-Planges had worn overalls, instead of the house coat of the surgeon or the wig of a barrister!

It is for this reason that Africanization of the senior posts of the Divisions of Forestry and Agriculture in particular did not begin until recently. Although the basic pay in most departments is the same, graduates shunned these posts like the plague; they were not going to become ' bushmen' not when for an extra year's study they could preen themselves in the mantle of ' Dr ' or aim for a judgeship. Independence in 1957, when the Gold Coast became Ghana and had suddenly to manage her own affairs, revealed the fact that though there was no lack of Ghanaian doctors and legal practitioners there was a considerable deficiency of senior officers in those vital Departments, Agriculture, Forestry, Fisheries, Animal Health and Geology. The cry of ' go home whiteman ' was shouted less often and more softly as it became evident that for a decade at least Ghana would need to lean heavily on the shoulders of the expatriate. In non-technical professions, especially the Administration, the District Commissioners, often lacking any special qualifications other than an arts degree, were soon to find themselves replaced by Ghanaians, also without any special qualifications, on the assumption, perhaps that administrators are born and not made. The successors to the District Commissioners, the Government Agents, have now been abolished. DC's have been re-born in title but not in function, and the present-day DC is a political appendage of the Government.

The six months' introductory bush experience weeds out the half-hearted Learner Rangers, leaving a hard core of youngsters who, if they do not love the forest, at least show no fear or dislike of it. It is these who enter the training school at Sunyani and are taught a multiplicity of subjects which comprise the science of forestry.

Forestry, like medicine, embraces many sciences. Unlike medicine, unlike most other professions, it combines wide theoretical knowledge with intense physical exertion, for the practice of forestry can be undertaken only in the forest. Those who know the forests of Ghana and West Africa, know that walking through them is a battle. The so-called dangerous animals of the forest we can dismiss; they are rarely seen. Snakes, many of them lethal, though common are even less obvious for they probably fear man at least as much as he fears them. In a survey among the major timber firms who employ thousands of workers who move, often barefooted, constantly in the forest, there were no fatal bites from snakes recorded in the two years 1958-60. But the prolific plant life —the tall stems of trees, the shrubs, the sparse herbs and the overall, inter-weaving, sometimes spiny, climbers, investing every growing thing—make the cutlass a necessity for a walk in the forest. Before he can manage the forest, the tropical forester must fight his way in (and out); the cool clean habitat of temperate climes, the ranks of trees set out with military precision, are not for him. So he has to be fit, the forester.

To qualify him for the highest professional posts, the budding forester needs a degree. At the University he will study the basic sciences: chemistry, physics, botany zoology and geology, as well as forest management, silviculture and forest engineering and surveying.

He will learn about soils, their structure and composition, how plants derive their nourishment from them, how animals till and enrich the soil and how the plant and animal world combine with the dead stuff of the soil to build up a forest.

He will learn how a plant grows and what it needs to grow; about the inter-dependence of plants and of plants and animals. And when he has absorbed the basic facts of life, he will come to the tree. He will spend three to four years looking at it, looking into, reading about, measuring, growing, planting, felling and cutting trees. His prayer will be the Prayer of the Trees:

You who pass by and would raise a hand against us, heed well our prayer before you harm us.

We are the fuel for your fires on cold nights, the shade protecting you from the fierce sun and our fruits are refreshments to quench your thirst and cheer you as you journey on.

We are the rafters of your roofs, the bodies of your boats, the seats of your stools and the boards of your beds.

We are the handles of your hoes, the gates of your homes, the wood of your cradles and the shells of your coffins.

We are the saviours of your soil from loss by rain and wind and to your soil we give richness and life for the benefit of all men.

We are the bread of kindness and the flower of beauty.

You who pass by, listen to our prayer and harm us not.

The world needs wood as it needs medicine and though you can synthetize many medicines, some of them from coal, which is fossilized wood, Man has not yet been able to synthetize wood. The production of wood by trees is possible only because of the process of photosynthesis (literally 'a making through light') whereby green plants in the presence of light are capable of growing and in growing make, among other things, wood. With all Man's knowledge he does not understand this phenomenon. We may split the atom but cannot prise from the plant's leaf the secret of photosynthesis.

The world therefore needs forests. It needs forests for other and more important reasons. Man can live without wood, but in the tropics he would soon die without trees. For trees not only make our cradles and our coffins, they make possible our agriculture, the climate and the soils without which Ghana could not grow its cocoa; without the forest Africa would be all desert.

The forester-in-training travels the world to learn how nature nurtures her forests, how man seeks to emulate her, and even to improve on her handiwork. Like any other crop, be it cocoa or cassava, trees have their likes and dislikes and different trees have different requirements. In West Africa there are some 600 different trees!

Growing trees is not then as easy as one might presume. And it takes time. A century must elapse before most trees are ready for the axe, ripe for the saw and in a form suitable for our cradles and our coffins. Whether the seeds are sown by Man and the young trees planted to make plantations; or whether the professional forester tends the natural forest, he needs trained officers to do the work. He needs the Forest Ranger.

The Learner Forest Ranger begins his forestry career as a school-boy with the General Certificate of Education, a little knowledge of basic science and no knowledge of the science of forestry. If he passes the entrance examination he enters the Forestry Training School at Sunyani. His course of training lasts three years. Half of this is spent in practical work in the forest, employing the lessons absorbed in the classroom. The Principal is a Conservator who is assisted by a Senior Master (Head Forester) and a Forestry Education Officer.

The Head Forester himself was a Learner, and for most of the years of his service, firstly as a Forest Ranger, then as a Senior Forest Ranger, as a Forester and then a Head Forester, he lived and worked in the forest. He has spent nights in a sodden tent, been afflicted with a thirst that could not be assuaged, has been lost and benighted, hungry and sometimes frightened. Now his job is to teach the young men that though the forest is a hard task-mistress, she is rewarding too.

Until 1958 the Learners learned in any old building. Until that date we were denied the money to build a weatherproof school and provide the simple apparatus required for efficient teaching. The School was run in association with the Department of Agriculture, in an old school at Sunyani, where the roof leaked and rain blew in through the glassless windows, and in an abandoned office at Mpraeso.

The unfortunate Learners had to find their own accommodation, no easy task in villages like Sunyani and Mpraeso. Often they had to be content with single, dark dirty rooms for which they were charged exorbitant rents. They too had to provide their own books and writing materials. There was no library and the little equipment needed had often to be cajoled on loan from a District Officer who was also short of compasses, chains, tents and other essentials of forestry life. Such was the parsimony that cursed the early days of the Department. Because we never had, it seemed to be assumed that we would never get and I was rapped over the knuckles when Brooks was Chief Conservator for daring to indent for adequate supplies of essentials. It was not until 1958 that a start was made in the building of a proper school and for the provision of proper and adequate materials for the teaching of forestry. This was the first major building development in the Department since its inception. Whatever else may have been accomplished since the securing of the permanent forest estate was so much façade without the trained staff to manage and develop that estate. Senior staff can plan, only Forest Rangers can execute the plans in the field. For years the quality of training lagged behind management and as a result the quality of the Ranger, through no fault of his own, was generally below that required for the proper implementation of the forest policy. ACF's with no experience of teaching were expected to turn a schoolboy into a Forest Ranger within a year in unsuitable surroundings and with insufficient equipment. It was not until the new school was finished in 1959 that a full three years' course could be undertaken with adequate staff and ample materials.

In the days, during and just after the second world war, while we were still completing the constitution of the Reserves, a Forest Ranger's job was a simple one: he needed to be literate, to have a sound working knowledge of surveying and to know his trees. As soon as we began to manage the Reserves on the basis of a sustained yield, however, considerably greater knowledge of scientific forestry was needed together with a general knowledge of the basic sciences upon which forestry depends. Many of the Forest Rangers did not receive as thorough a training in these subjects as the work now expected of them demands.

In the purely protective days when a Ranger's duties were

mainly pounding the boundaries to see if they were still there and in the condition reported by the Forest Guards, each Ranger held a charge of several hundred square miles of Reserves. He spent his life walking his Range. Today, although we concede that the protection of the forest estate is our primary concern, its management is important too. A Ranger may now find himself tied to a single Reserve, destined to survey and map it tree-by-tree and to supervise the constant silvicultural improvements required. Work is now so concentrated and exacting that while our estate could be efficiently protected by fifty Rangers doing little else but protective work, the task of management *now* requires three times that number and within a few years will need at least 300, or one for each twenty square miles of the permanent forest estate in the high forest zone.

Promotion within the Ranger cadre is almost automatic and rarely does brilliance shine so brightly as to upset the normal progress of seniority. The dullards and slackers are usually passed over until by increased application they reinstate themselves. Some never do. Cleverness, or brilliance, is not sought in a profession where thoroughness and an ability to rough it are primary assets. Indeed, the brilliant men may be at a disadvantage. F. K. Chey was one whose brilliance could not help him to stay the course and I have known at least two others of similar stamp who will never make the topmost grade. Forestry operations cover such large areas, and are impossible economically to check entirely, that considerable reliance is placed on the executive—the Forest Ranger. His costs, checked at the monthly pay-out do not necessarily indicate a job well done or otherwise and it is often that a major defection remains hidden for a year or two. Ranger Amoah hands over his Range to his relief Ranger Mensah. The handing-over notes certifying that specific works have been done are signed by both men. A year or so hence Ranger Mensah discovers that farm No. 7 in the Konkong Reserve cannot be found. He reports the fact. The ACF deputes his Forester to investigate and it finally transpires that the farm boundaries in this Reserve have not been cleaned for years. Thus a mesh of tangled deceit, which involves labourers, Forest Guards and Forest Rangers, is gradually revealed, and a few increments lost!

The young men who cheerfully dedicated their lives to the

forest are the salt of the earth and they were, perhaps, often taken too much for granted. Looking back I know that few of the Forest Rangers I knew have any regrets at their choice of career. There is little fun in life in the forest until it has been lived. Then one derives immense pleasure in reviewing the discomforts, the hardships and dangers past.

To be lost in the bush is one of the least pleasant experiences. Mr E. K. Safo, now Senior Master at the Training School describes his experience of being lost in the following account:

Short cuts are often risky, especially in a forest to which one is a complete stranger. It was in the month of October when the night thunder-storms and rains were at their peak in the remote, dense and inaccessible forest of the Western Province during my early days as a Forest Ranger, that I received instructions from the District Forest Officer to leave my range for another which was new to me. I was instructed to carry out a survey in the Tano Nimri Forest Reserve.

I left my Range headquarters very early in the morning on foot with four labourers. We arrived at our camping village Mooso, some twenty miles away late in the afternoon. This village was near the River Tano which was then heavy with water. I went to greet the village chief as the native custom has it, and then started making enquiries about the path leading to the starting point of the survey. I noticed that the elder townsmen were somewhat reluctant to show me the path, but thought little of it.

The day for the work, a Friday, started gloomily. Although I had instructed my personal boy to give me a very heavy breakfast of ampesi and nkontomire and to make a parcel of two heavy gari balls for my lunch in the field, he overslept, and I was obliged to forgo breakfast and to make my own gari balls. I therefore left the hut with heavy heart and empty stomach with my cape, compass and the two inexpertly made gari balls in my haversack and a full waterbottle. As we went by some of the villagers muttered and pointed at us, but we hardy and weather-beaten foresters paid no attention.

We succeeded in reaching the Reserve boundary after struggling through entanglements of lianes and creepers and wading through marshes and finally being ferried across the swollen Tano River in a canoe. We began our work straight away and by midday had cut a distance of some eighty chains which was good going considering the wet conditions and the dense thorny nature of the vegetation. We had a break and ate our lunch and without delay resumed our work. We were traversing a steep downward slope when the chain went over a coiled sleeping black cobra. In anger the snake sprang valleywards in the direction of the front chain-man. I closed my eyes and shouted 'God help us!' When I next opened my eyes I saw both chainmen lying on the ground terri-fied but unhurt. The snake had gone. At this point, after we had covered ninety-five chains I decided we would stop work and return to the village. One of the labourers told me that he knew of a footpath not far away which we could follow back to the village. I was a little doubtful but not relishing the return journey over the line we had cut, we followed him hopefully hoping that this short cut would get us home before nightfall.

It was then about 3 p.m. At 5 p.m. we were still seeking the footpath. From time to time a roar of thunder rumbled in the distance and as dusk began to fall the rain started pouring down. The crickets and other insects started their varied noises which signified the end of the day. I knew then that we would not see Mooso that night. Fortunately we had passed near an old aban-doned farm during the morning and even more fortunately we managed to find our way there. Had it not been for one particular labourer who was a smoker and carried matches we should have gone to bed in the open, a most dismal prospect. We made a torch from palm branches and with much trouble got it lighted. One of the labourers bearing the torch went ahead while the rest of us followed him hand in hand as the followers of the magic swan. At last we reached the farm. It was 7 p.m. by my watch. We made a fire and sat around it and dried our sodden garments. One of the labourers then climbed into the little leaf-thatched barn in the farm and brought a few cobs of dry corn. This we roasted in a broken pot. I was served on a wet banana leaf and I enjoyed my frugal meal up to a certain point when I felt that my teeth could no more stand the chewing of the hard roasted corn grains. A place was then prepared for me in the barn to sleep. The com-pass was my pillow, the cape my blanket and scores of mice my bedmates. The night seemed endless. I fell asleep and woke and found it was only 10 p.m. I lay in the darkness counting the seconds, minutes and hours, and now and then a mouse would run over my face. Finally I fell asleep and did not again awake until the labourers awoke me at 6 a.m. Breakfast of roast corn was prepared and when we had eaten we set out for Mooso.

After some time we heard drumming in the distance and soon afterwards we came to the river. Not long afterwards while following the river we glimpsed three men laboriously paddling up-stream. We hailed them. They saw us and shouted for joy. They paddled towards us and kept repeating ' Won ni, won ni, won ni' meaning ' Here they are, here they are.' So were we rescued and taken back to Mooso where we were told that Friday was a sacred day and that no one must cut anything in the forest; they knew that we had met with some misfortune. When I told them of our series of misfortunes beginning with my lack of breakfast on the Friday morning, they were not surprised. Undoubtedly the gods were angry, they said.

WHAT IS FORESTRY?

As one of the most eminent present-day tropical foresters remarks : *If the temperate forester frequently complains he hasn't a clue, the forester in the Tropical High Forest does not even know how or where to start looking for clues.*

The forester's troubles spring from the slow and irregular growth of trees. There are some trees which have been known to achieve twenty feet height growth in their first year, and four feet girth at breast height has been recorded in twenty-five years by others. But seldom is a crop of trees grown for timber ready for the axe during the lifetime of the man who planted them.

Forestry is a science and a business. As a science it must follow accepted rules; as a business it must pay. The use to which the forest will be put will depend on the policy of the owner and this needs considerable thought for changes in policy can be as cata-strophic as changing horses in mid-stream. Yields of agricultural and horticultural crops can reasonably be estimated in accordance with the kind of crop being grown and the nature of the soil. Where forestry has been practised assiduously it is also possible to forecast, with fair accuracy, the yield. Where the practice of growing and managing trees has gone on long enough as it has in Europe for centuries, this can be done.

In West Africa forestry is young, less than fifty years old, and the clues which the temperate forester knows are available if he can but find them, are as elusive to the tropical forester as the legendary ' little people '. The horticulturist plans his crops according to his markets and his capacity from season to season. The forester cannot do this. His yield is often unknown; his season is seventy years or more. A forest will yield so much, how much it is often impossible to determine accurately. In Europe it is possible to calculate with fair accuracy how much. Temperate trees produce rings annually which can be counted in the standing trees by means of an increment borer. In the tropics, where trees rarely produce annual rings, and where forestry is too young to know how big a tree will grow in a given time, the sustained yield of the forest cannot accurately be determined.

The tropical forester is usually in a position in which he has his crop at or near maturity, but cannot calculate the yield, not only because the trees do not produce annual rings, but because there are so many different kinds of trees which do not produce annual rings. The temperate forester deals with half a dozen species, often with a single species, whose growth characteristics may have been known for centuries; his tropical counterpart manages a forest comprising two or three hundred species inextricably mixed and of all ages from one to two hundred years.

Because the increment or growth of a tree is generally slow, it is necessary that its assessment be carefully done. One overcutting may upset management (and profits) for a decade. The forester's problem is difficult also because his yield, unlike that of the horti-culturist, for example, is invisible, as a thin sheath of wood beneath the bark. It can never be measured precisely for a whole forest. When incremental rates are known, by individual tree measure-ments or, for larger areas, by the constant re-measurement of sample areas, even after the figures have been collated with the locality, for different soils, different aspects, different elevations, produce different yields, even then the calculations are little better than shrewd estimates.

Before the proper management of Ghana's forests could be started, it was necessary to understand something of the nature of the forest. That it was not the same throughout the 31,000 square miles of the high forest zone was obvious to 'Timber' Thompson in the beginning. Whether the differing forms of forest occurred in clear-cut zones, was something that had to be determined on the ground. His early reconnaissance established the fact that in the south-west the forest was 'moist evergreen tropical forest' similar to that which he had known in India. As his travels took him northwards so the character of the forest changed, it gradually became more deciduous, as the climate changed from an almost constantly wet one to one with a marked dry season, the trees reacted and lost their leaves in the dry season. Species which were dominant in the wet forest were replaced by others which preferred a drier climate and which could withstand the equivalent of a winter period.

In considering the management of these forests, the forester must estimate his markets. Existing ones he knows; tomorrow's he can estimate fairly well. But what of the markets fifty years hence? In the past century mahogany has remained a best-seller and its qualities are such, and its name so firmly established throughout the world, that it is likely to continue in demand. Much the same can be said of the related cedars. Odum (Iroko) has never had a chance to show its merits to the world. The Government jealously guards this species and continues to preclude it from the world's markets for reasons which are clear only to the Government! Elsewhere in Africa it is exported as fast as demand dictates.

Odum is supposed to be the traditional wood of the Ghanaian and popular superstition appears to demand that it must at all costs be preserved. Two to three decades ago the pitsawyer who produced most of the lumber used in Ghana, chose Odum. He chose it for several reasons. It grows to great size, is well shaped and lacks buttresses; it is resistant to insect attack and fungal decay and it takes a fine finish. But during the war when pitsawing was greatly expanded the sawyers discovered that other timbers easier to saw commanded the same price as Odum. Tradition was speedily deserted.

The present local demand for Odum lumber is small and in the face of increasing demand for softer more economic woods, it is not likely to increase. Thus the annual increment of Odum is considerably in excess of its annual consumption, which means that there is a constant wastage of timber grown too old, dying and rotting, apart from the thousands of trees destroyed annually in the farmers' fires. There are vast quantities of Odum in the Reserves; their increment is wasted. Sawmills do not want massive old trees however sound and straight they may be. Their carriages, lifting equipment and saws are not designed to deal with monster logs.

In spite of the advice of the Chief Conservator, Odum may not be exported. In 1958, the ban was lifted for a trial period of one year. In response many firms logged and sawed and transported thousands of pieces of Odum when suddenly, without warning, apology, or explanation, the ban was reimposed. What a waste of a valuable natural asset!

The market for Wawa, which at present comprises over fifty per cent of all log exports, cannot be predicted. In little more than a decade its exports have rocketed from almost nothing to over 12 million cubic feet! It might plummet even more rapidly and suddenly. But these wanted species represent only a tiny fraction of those available. A list as long as this page, of other, some more common, species could easily be compiled which for all practical purposes are so much waste wood. What is the forester to do with these?

As Thompson's successors drove their booted feet over the rugged terrain of the forest belt, no larger than the southern counties of England, but rough, hot, and wet and disease-ridden, their notes, summarized and clarified by C. J. Taylor in 1952, revealed a fairly clear zonation and pattern of species. Taylor divides the high forest into two main zones: the evergreen rain forest in the south-west and the moist deciduous forest elsewhere. The latter he sub-divides into three sub-zones of varying degrees of dryness reflecting a change in indicator species. The significance of the latter is illustrated by the absence of two dominant ones *Triplochiton* (Wawa: Obeche) and *Celtis* (Esa) from the rain forest and their dominance throughout the moist deciduous zone.

What was less readily apparent was the structure of the forest, even to those who had walked through it and lived in it for most of their service. The classic description is as follows: The closed high forest of Ghana and West Africa is multi-storied. At the top there is an open storey, or layer, of emergent trees; a little below comes a more closed, sometimes completely closed, layer comprising the crowns of numerous dominant and sub-dominant trees; considerably lower down is a relatively closed canopy of understorey trees and finally a sparse layer of shrubs beneath which is a scattering of herbs. Throughout the woof and warp of this layering runs the tangled skein of regeneration fighting its way to the top.

The establishment of research centres in each vegetation zone began properly just before the end of the second world war, and the detailed examination of the tree vegetation therein, supplemented by the information gained from the sampling of all the Forest Reserves, revealed two major variations on this theme. The presence of large numbers of young trees, poles, and only a few emergents and dominants, had frequently been remarked on and regarded as secondary forest, that is the kind of forest which grows when the virgin forest is felled and the area is left alone. Similarly, there was forest in which the upper canopies showed a preponderance of very large and old trees with little growing beneath them, which was considered to be a young stage in secondary regrowth, resulting from farming activities.

The occurrence of these variations in areas where Man's influence had never been felt for half a century, however, was evidence of a cyclical theory developed by the French forester Aubreville, each cycle representing continuous stages in the development of the tropical high forest, and having nothing to do with shifting cultivation.

The major research centres contained every stage of the forest. As observations were continued year after year it gradually became apparent that successful concentrated natural regeneration could be reasonably assured only where the main canopies are well represented. Under these conditions it was gradually confirmed that natural regeneration by suitable canopy manipulation could give a forest considerably richer than any existing forest. Good results could probably be obtained in less favourable areas where the canopies were broken, while in the south-west (in the rain forest) the dearth of seed-bearing mother trees precluded natural regeneration and required a supplementary artificial means of regenerating the forest.

The study and treatment of sample plots in the decade after the second world war provided a note of discouragement as well as one of encouragement. Unable to assess the ages of trees accurately because of the lack of annual rings, we had made estimates of growth rates which allowed twenty years for an average valuable tree to pass through a two-feet girth class i.e. that such a tree put on an average of one and one fifth inches in girth each year. Annual remeasurements of marked trees I these plots, however, gradually revealed the depressing fact that on the average it took twenty-five years to pass through a two-feet girth class. Existing yields based on the higher estimate thus had to be reduced sub-staintially and future estimates curtailed.

Some of the plots had been thinned and the enveloping and constricting mass of climbers cleared. We found that the response of young trees to climber cutting was to show a considerable in-crease in the rates of growth. *Ergo*, thinnings and climber-cutting could accelerate growth in the natural forest. We knew, from our one per cent samplings, that the forest was rich in young valuable species and it was decided that in areas insufficiently rich to justify the *concentrated* and expensive treatment by the Tropical Shelter-wood System, climber cutting and thinning would be introduced to increase the yield three-fold within an estimated period of thirty to forty years. Most of the permanent forest estate is being treated in this way.

In the 1,000 square miles of rain forest where valuable mother trees are so sparse that the lush natural regeneration which Ghana needs to improve her forests cannot be achieved, artificial enrich-ment by planting is being undertaken. Because men are expensive to employ (the labourer's basic rate has risen by 550 per cent in the last twenty years; the professional Forest Officer's pay by sixty per cent) and need even more expensive supervision, the cost of the Tropical Shelterwood System and enrichment planting is high and necessitates heavy capital outlay for high returns three or four generations hence. Only improvement thinnings will pay off within a man's lifetime. To find out about the forest, two major steps were taken. The first, beginning in 1929, was the enumeration of every Forest Reserve. Parallel lines were cut through the Reserves and an area encompassed by the lines equal to one per cent of the Reserve area enumerated so that every tree within that area was identified, measured and recorded. It should then have been possible by a simple x 100 multiplication to assess the num-bers of all species of all sizes within each Reserve. That it did not will be made plain later.

Of all the tasks which I have been set, I detested enumeration more than any. I have made roads in Holland and dug ditches there for no pay; I drilled and was drilled in the Army and have lain all night in the open as part of my training; I have practised five-finger exercises on the piano by the hour; walked the baby all night; cleaned out a septic tank; been a returning officer in an Ashanti election on the eve of Independence! None of these did I dislike so heartily as the labour of leading an enumeration party.

It was my first job when I took over from Cansdale. I travelled by lorry from Juaso to the Bobiri Reserve some twenty miles away while my ten carriers found their own way there and had set up camp by the time I arrived. Bright and early next day, the carriers, wearing only a loin cloth and each armed with a cutlass, began the arduous task of line-cutting, following a bearing laid off by Forest Ranger M. D. Owusu on his prismatic compass. They cut, with scarcely a pause in daylight hours, Saturdays and Sundays alike (there was no overtime!) for weeks on end. We followed and enumerated. Ranger Owusu enumerated; I looked and learned.

All bookings were in Twi, not the easiest language for the white man to learn, but one which I had been directed to learn and upon which my future increments depended. It is a tonic language and the same word pronounced in different ways can mean very different things. This occasionally led to some embarrassing moments. Not only was the language new, so were the trees.

A degree course in Forestry teaches the bare bones of the science; it has nothing to do with its exotic manifestations four thousand miles from the lecture room. In the Bobiri I began my forestry, again, with the memorizing of hundreds of Twi names together with their scarcely less confusing botanical equivalents.

As a botanist—not a good one as I have explained—I was used to determinations by the characteristics of leaves, flowers and fruits, the accepted bases of botanical identification. Now, all I was faced with was the bark of innumerable trees, few of which had diagnostic characters, and most of which were thickly encrusted with a vigorous growth of climbers and epiphytes. I carried a cutlass in my belt. Whenever an identification was made, either by Owusu or one of the tree-spotters, its name was shouted out to be recorded in the field book, and I would fight my way over to that particular tree through the wild tangle of vegetation, take a swipe at it with the cutlass and try, mentally, to correlate the colour, smell and taste of the slash so revealed with the Twi name. Having laboriously recorded this in my note book and ascertained from Owusu the botanical binominal equivalent and written a brief description of the slash characters, we repeated the process *ad infinitum* it seemed, and certainly *ad nauseum*.

If the tree spotters did not know a tree they concocted a name, but after I had laboriously ran a few of these down to obscure plants whose habitat was on the sea shore or in some other unlikely habitat, we agreed that 'unknowns' must be called 'unknown'. In such an instance we summoned a conference of all within shouting distance. Line-cutters, the Forest Guard, Owusu and my helpless self, would then cut, look, sniff and taste, often to no purpose. Down went the name in the book 'Unknown'. Cluttered up as I was with a helmet, notebook, and cutlass, sweat running endlessly down my face and neck, flies and sweat bees ceaselessly sucking at the sweat; hot, confused, and with only the vaguest clue of what was happening, I still contrived time to thumb through Irvine's *Plants of the Gold Coast*. This preserved my sanity on many such occasions.

Not only was the text arranged in alphabetical order, listing most of Ghana's trees, shrubs and herbs, but it contained vernacular indices, including one in Twi. In my slow heat-flustered way, ignoring, because there was nothig else I could do, my constantly sodden condition from crown to toes, I was able now and then to do a bit of constructive work with the assistance of Irvine.

What an enormous debt present-day scientists, teachers and administrators owe to the small band of people dedicated to an ideal, who throughout their service took the trouble not only to find out about the unknown but to publish the results of what must often have been considerable labour! As one who believes firmly in the dictum that work is a necessary evil, I have never ceased to wonder at, and to be grateful for, the amount of patient sustained hard labour which the compilation of such books as Irvine's *Plants of the Gold Coast* and Dalziel's even more encyclopaedic *Useful Plants of West Tropical Africa*, has involved. I have studied and cherished Irvine more than any other book I ever possessed, for it is poetry and science, medicine and art, all in one.

Part of Irvine's introduction to his book is worth reading by anyone interested in Africa, expressing succinctly what I would like to say about it :

Those who take an interest in the plants around them invariably begin by asking their names. Africans are anxious to know the 'English' names of Gold Coast plants, often forgetting that very few of the plants found here grow in Europe at all. Europeans, on the other hand, find no alternative between learning the long scientific names and many equally difficult vernacular names. This work attempts to relate the two. The vernacular names of plants on the Gold Coast are legion, as anyone attempting to learn them realizes. Moreover there is great confusion among them, and it is to help clear up this confusion that the names have been collected and printed. In the past they have been handed down by oral tradition. The ever-increasing spread of European civilization and the English language has led to a dissolution of tribal life resulting in a great mixing of tribes. Many children are being educated away from the homes of their ancestors, and the vernacular names of plants are rapidly being lost. . . . It would be regrettable if the people of the Gold Coast lost their vernacular names of plants, and with them, what is more important, all the knowledge of their uses and the plant lore which are wrapped up in them. . . . Sometimes one finds that the same name may be applied to more than one plant. . . . Also, one plant may be known by several different names in one place, or by entirely different names in adjacent districts in the same language area. Sometimes the meanings of these plant names throw light on the use or appearance of the plant, or on native ideas or beliefs about it.

With so few sources of information available a compilation was practically out of the question. The information here is based mainly on field collections. Over twelve hundred and fifty specimens of plants have been collected and duplicates and triplicates have been sent to the Royal Botanical Gardens, Kew, and the Imperial Forestry Institute, Oxford. Actual specimens of most of the plants can be seen by visiting the Achimota herbarium or the herbarium of the Forestry Department at Kumasi, or that of the Agricultural Department at Aburi. . . .

This book is being published in this relatively incomplete state

to stimulate interest and inquiry among potential investigators. . . .
It is hoped that after several years of gradual accumulation of
further material of this sort, a more complete and accurate second
edition will be produced which will be of more permanent value.

Alas, an Irvine or a Dalziel appears but rarely, and it is sad to
record that since 1930, when Irvine's book was published, there
seems to have been insufficient enthusiasm to produce an up-to-
date edition, and *Plants of the Gold Coast* has long since been out
of print.

If the unknown tree was not too big to be felled, we felled it,
hacked off the leaves (flowers and fruits if any) placed them in a
plant press and went on to the next tree. The number of 'unknowns' became depressingly large. At the same time the list of
knowns, unknown to me, seemed to be endless.

The labour of moving along a cut line was considerable to the
uninitiated. Not only was there the usual collection of hazards, the
indecently profuse young growth, and endless climbers, some
spiny, some with recurved thorns the size and sharpness of an
eagle's talons; there were also fallen trees, some so big and soft with
rot that they could not be climbed but had to be circumvented;
there were the numerous saplings cut at knee height leaving each
cut end as sharp as a chisel; my knees were perpetually bloody. In
addition there were the unknown hazards. To me there was always
a cobra behind every tree, coiled in every declivity, entwined about
every branch. There was in fact always at least one species
of bloodsucking insect only too eager for my young thick
blood.

The efficient enumeration party can reckon to cut, survey and
record about a mile a day; it depends on the terrain, the forest, the
tree-spotter and the Ranger. For the first few days we covered
about a quarter of this daily; I was learning. I learned slowly but
our pace gradually quickened as I began to recognize the more
obvious species. At the end of the working day, I was sweat-sodden,
aching, weary, thirsty as though I had never drunk before, hungry
and in a vile mood. The constant stopping and starting to slash, to
note, to smell, to taste, to learn, was anathema to my restless
nature. When the work was over we had to retrace our steps over
the cut line. The carriers were happy then, God knows why, their

pay was but one shilling a day and nothing found, not even shelter.

After two weeks of this torture, I gave up and returned to Juaso to recover. So glad was I to get out of the damp endless gloom of the forest and to be relieved of the physical tedium of its enumeration, that I walked blissfully all the way back to Juaso. Physically I must have been about as fit as I have ever been. I walked the venom out of my system that day! There was a lot of enumeration to do; I did no more than my share. Others like Chidlow Vigne and his party of Cameron, Duff and Horwood, spent months on end doing *nothing* else and saner men than these I have never met. Vigne was probably the finest forest botanist in Africa. A Master of Science (Yale) he was an enthusiast and a knowledge-able one, yet a complete extrovert: if things were wrong he righted them, or got them righted; if one was an idiot, one was told. He lived the full life unencumbered by introspection or pettiness. He was honest and forthright and there was no cant in him; he was a pleasure to work with. There were few plants he did not know; and he knew them feature by feature, regarding them almost as an artist will regard a rare portrait. When he identified something he saw it as a complete entity: leaves; size, shape, venation, orientation; fruits and flowers he saw as similar entities. He knew, and he gave his knowledge freely and dispassionately. I shall never confuse the family *Plumbaginaceae* with another because once when we were relieving ourselves noisily into a Plumbago bush, he said casually, 'notice the glandular hairs on the calyx; absolutely typical.'

Petty bickering lost us a good man and his unrivalled knowledge. Though primarily a botanist, properly directed he would have made a first class silviculturist, but for reasons at which I can only guess, Captain Marshall abolished his post in 1936, thereby wasting Vigne's time and losing us some ten years of silvicultural time.

When our one per cent enumeration surveys were almost completed, and we began to utilize the information they gave us in determining growing stock, increment and yield, it was discovered that one per cent x 100 did not equal 100 per cent! One per cent enumerations we found were too small to be statistically reliable: they did not cover a large enough sample. As a result some of our yields were grossly inaccurate. A small error when multiplied by 100 gives a whopper. We had to start all over again to measure our estate.

This time we employed five per cent methods employing stratified sampling in accordance with the new science of statistics which has revolutionized our management thinking. The Working Plans Branch established in 1947 has devoted most of its field work to random sampling in order to obtain a more complete picture of the forest and its growing stock which is the basis of sound management.

Perpetual though the tropical forest may be when it is left alone, regenerating itself without Man's help, it is not as efficient as we would like it to be. Most of the wood which it grows is of no use to Man at present; not even for firewood. One could not give it away.

Light is the limiting factor in silviculture; insufficient reduces rates of growth; too much encourages excessive weed growth, and weeds in the forest include giants of two hundred feet in height! To find out about light in its relation to the forest and how best to regulate it, Research Centres of a third of a square mile each were selected in each high forest District. Treatments employing different densities of light were introduced by felling and killing by poisoning useless and unwanted trees.

For some years District Officers became part-time silviculturists observing and recording results which the silviculturist himself checked and condensed and from which was evolved a system of natural regeneration called the Tropical Shelterwood System. In good high forest with ample seed trees of the right species this system is helping to achieve Clause 2 of the forest policy viz: *The management of permanent forest resources by methods that will achieve maximum productivity and value on the basis of a sustained yield.*

This system can succeed only in good forest, of which there is not a great area in Ghana; it is also expensive and necessitates an ever-increasing annual commitment of expensive treatment and a steadily increasing denial of part of the yield till the end of the rotation, i.e., those trees of the middle and small size classes must be left until regeneration is complete. The expected returns in increased numbers of valuable species in a reduced rotation are seven

to eight times that in the average untouched forest, but whereas
an annual cut would be permitted elsewhere, the achievement of
a rich even-aged forest under this system means a wait of anything
up to one hundred years before the final felling.

In the relatively poor rain forest, enrichment planting began in
1951 and soon indicated that such forest could be enriched by
planting nursery-grown young trees in lines. The young trees must
be given ample light and all lower storey species that interrupt the
source of light are poisoned. This means of improving the forest
must be carried out only after the forest has been exploited, which
means that no further felling is permitted until the end of the
rotation, i.e., until the young trees have reached felling size in
seventy to one hundred years.

In the average forest, i.e., about three-quarters of the permanent
forest estate in the high forest zone, general thinning by poisoning
and cutting out the useless climbers and weed-trees that hinder
the growth of the valuable trees, is standard treatment. To mini-
mize cost and reduce the time spent in the forest, this improvement is combined with a hundred per cent enumeration survey and
the stock mapping of individual valuable trees, and is accordingly
known as the Combined Operation.

THE FOREST, COCOA AND MAN

The road map of Ghana, which finds a place in every Government
office there, shows the country as roughly oblong in shape and
about the same size as Britain. There are two sharply defined divisions lying north and south of a prominent mountainous ridge
which begins near the estuary of the great Volta River in the south-
east corner. This ridge extends north-west to where the Volta
meets the frontier with the French Ivory Coast.

Except in this north-west corner, there is a fairly sharp transition between the vegetation north of the high ground and that to
the south. From a line representing the northern face of the scarp
to the northern limit of Ghana is *savannah*. This usually has a
park or orchard-like appearance with more grass than trees; the
former taller than a man when mature; the latter often stunted
and twisted. In the north-west corner of Ashanti, where the scarp

line is broken, the *savannah* zone has moved east and south, en-
filading the line and breaking the smooth course of delimitation.
This apart, south of the line lies the closed high forest. The
savannah area covers two-thirds of the country (60,083 square
miles); the closed high forest area one-third (31,760 square
miles).

Until the end of the nineteenth century, when cocoa was introduced into Ghana, the southern zone had probably remained un-
changed for thousands of years. It could with truth be described
as *closed* forest and extended in a belt that was unbroken except
for small scattered food-farm areas, from very near the coast up to
the line of the north-west escarpment and right across the whole
width of the country. Since the introduction of cocoa, the destruction of the high forest has proceeded at an ever-increasing pace.
Today, we are near the end of it. Within a decade or so the high
forest will have gone, 26,000 square miles of it destroyed in little
over half a century. Only the Forest Reserves, protected by law,
guarded and patrolled, stand as bastions of prosperity.

In the northern *savannah* zone the only closed high forest is that
which extends in narrow belts along the rivers and bigger streams;
this river-tain or fringing forest is similar in form and composition
to the high forest of the south and lends some support to the view
that at one time closed high forest extended over a substantial
part of the north.

The closed high forest, untouched by Man, is perpetual. It will
not burn and its regeneration, although slow, is sure and complete.
Where Man introduces fire and felling, the forest is easily
destroyed. This has happened in the south. If high forest once
flourished in the north, Man must have destroyed it, and to do so
he must have had widespread farming communities in areas
which today appear on the road-map as blanks, designated ' uninhabited '. There is no doubt whatever that the north is what the
south will look like if its high forest is utterly destroyed.

The effects of the removal of the forest are many. It is due to
shifting cultivation and there is a pressure of population on the
land, *savannah* conditions speedily ensue, and this is but a step
from desert. In the past, there has been no wide-spread land
hunger, and the system of shifting cultivation, which is a rota-
tional system of agriculture, was not harmful. With the prosperity

which cocoa has brought; with the ever-increasing area planted with cocoa; with a reduction in the infantile death-rate and an increase in the life-span of the people, there is less and less forest left for more and more people; people, moreover, who have bigger appetites because they are more healthy. In these circumstances, shifting cultivation is a menace.

It is a menace, not only because it prevents the forest from regenerating, which it will do even if it is cut down and burnt, given time; it is a menace because on the present scale it is like an unchecked cancer. A few small scattered areas of devastated forest have little mass effect. Many such areas let in the wind and rain and sun, all enemies of the soil if unchecked, with calamitous effects on the soil and on the local climate. A plantation of cocoa is a low forest in itself. Left alone it would play the part of a low forest, maintaining a more or less equable climate, preserving the soil and maintaining water supplies which emanate from the soil. A plantation of cocoa, however, is vulnerable to the Harmattan; it lacks the resiliency of the high forest; it cannot achieve what the high forest achieves, and still produce cocoa.

A cocoa plantation, moreover, has to serve a more immediate purpose. It has to yield cocoa. The goodness of the cocoa beans which are removed when ripe and that of the thick pods which are usually destroyed, represents a robbery of the soil which does not occur in untouched forest. There, *all* the goodness which the trees absorb from the soil is returned to it: everything that grows, dies and decays, and its richness returns to the soil whence it came. Some eight million tons of cocoa beans have been grown in Ghana and exported. They represent the richness of Ghana. They also represent much of the richness of Ghana's soil, which basically is the wealth of Ghana. According to Charter, the removal of these eight million tons of beans has meant a loss to the soil of about half a million tons of sulphate of ammonia, 600,000 tons of superphospate of lime and 300,000 tons of sulphate of potash. None of these essential plant nutrients has ever been replaced.

Therein lies the significance of this fact: *that the production of cocoa in Ghana, in spite of continually increasing areas of cocoa being grown has remained almost static for thirty years.* Disease, especially *swollen shoot*, has played a big part in depressing production, but in view of the vast areas of forest destroyed and

Above: Learner forest rangers. *Bottom left:* A hunter who claims to have killed more than a hundred elephants. *Bottom right:* The Aframsu Falls in the Bandai Hills forest reserve.

The end of a forest elephant.

planted largely with cocoa, declining soil fertility must also be a major cause. It seems evident that present output, in the region a quarter-million tons per annum, is near the peak. As little unreserved forest remains to be planted, it is expected (Charter prophesied this) that a decline in output must soon become evident, a decline which may cripple Ghana's economy within a far shorter period than that in which cocoa established it.

It seems unlikely that increased areas planted with cocoa can, under present conditions, permanently increase output. Only a resuscitation of soil fertility, allied with disease control, can achieve this. What has been taken from the soil must be put back. This is the first principle of economic agriculture. The Forest Reserves, representing the permanent forest estate, now cover one fifth of the area of the high forest zone, the cocoa-growing zone. The consensus of world forestry opinion, considers that such a proportion is sufficient to ensure that climate and water supplies are maintained.

Today, the Forest Reserves stand as the sole bastions against economic disaster. Within little more than half-a-century the forest of which they formed part has been almost entirely destroyed. Flying over southern Ghana today, one can easily pick-out the Reserves: they are the only untouched areas of forest remaining; their canopies remain closed and within what we term the closed forest zone, only these represent the *closed high forest*. The rest is farm, food and cocoa farms and abandoned farms whose fertility is almost exhausted, which in the populous areas are fast degenerating into *savannah* and semi-desert areas.

On the edge of the scarp, where the hot dry northern climate can be felt, this degeneration is swift and irreversible. The soil has gone, and even if carefully protected, it is doubtful if these areas would ever regenerate themselves. To mitigate the severity of the northern climate, in particular to temper the hot, dry, dust-laden Harmattan which annually sweeps southwards from the Sahara Desert, the Forest Reserves along the scarp were established as barrier Reserves, with their long axes at right angles to the wind. Although these Reserves are not always contiguous, they do form practically a continuous barrier of high forest, up to 250 feet high

TWB   F

and five to ten miles wide, mainly on the high ground, to blunt the impact of this desiccating wind.

The effects of the Harmattan are rarely felt within the high forest. Where the barrier Reserves lie, high on the escarpment, however, its ultimate effect is to strip the leaves from the trees. This does not happen at once, nor does it happen to all trees; some resist it. The forest suffers but it does not die. Cocoa, thus subjected, yields little cocoa and has a short life.

The effect of the Harmattan can be catastrophic to agriculture, and there is no man-made palliative: we cannot air-condition the climate. Yet, if cocoa is to flourish, the Harmattan must be gentled. How this can be effected is better understood if we appreciate how a tree is nourished.

Like nearly all green plants, a tree derives part of its nourishment from the soil in the form of chemical salts dissolved in water, and part from the atmosphere. By the interaction of the chlorophyll, which gives the green colour to leaves, and the carbon dioxide which is a constituent of the air, carbohydrates (sugars, starch) and ultimately proteins, are manufactured: this is photosynthesis. The minerals from the soil complete the manufacture and the water which conveys the minerals for elaboration within the leaves, circulates the manufactured food materials throughout the tree. There must be a constant movement of water from the soil to the leaves. Only a small proportion of this water is needed for re-circulation, the rest is released into the atmosphere through special vents in the leaves called stomata.

We lack precise data on the amount of water which is lost by this process called transpiration. Experiments have indicated that as much as a hundred gallons of water can be transpired by a mature tree actively growing in a single day. This represents a daily loss of water per acre to the atmosphere from the kind of forest which grows in the barrier Reserves of up to five hundred gallons or nearly two tons in weight. As there are about a thousand square miles of these Reserves, the daily loss of water to the atmosphere is in the region of three hundred million gallons or roughly one and a quarter million tons.

The dry Harmattan sucks this up avidly and its dryness is reduced correspondingly; so is its speed as it becomes heavier with water vapour, and its potency as a plant destroyer. High temperatures accelerate transpiration and as the Harmattan is hot from the desert the effect on the vast acreage of leaf is that of a vast water-cooler, the clay ones which by their porosity evaporate part of their contents and by this loss of energy, lose heat themselves and cool their contents. A moister and cooler Harmattan is less dangerous to the shade-loving cocoa.

Looking at the road map of Ghana today, the forester observes two significant things: the solid comforting pattern of green in the south, the Forest Reserves; and the blank white areas immediately to the north-east, which the map proclaims to be 'uninhabited'. The former are a guarantee that the latter will not spread. To the forester, especially one who has had a hand, and two feet, in the often painful work of selecting and demarcating these Forest Reserves, this is a stimulating thought.

On Reserve selection and demarcation, often deep in the untraversed forest, alone in a tent at night, the thin veil of a mosquito net was often the only barrier between me and the imagined terrors of the night. Hundreds of nights I was the victim of my own imagination; no harm ever befell me, but the faith I placed in that mosquito net was considerable. It would usually keep out mosquitoes and other biting insects, small snakes and little mammals. It once let in a six-inch centipede and occasionally small stinging furies. On the night a leopard walked through my tent, it was only the mosquito net which preserved my sanity.

The Forest Reserves are scarcely more tangible; they cannot keep anything out, and Man can easily destroy them; by destroying them he destroys himself. Alas, the opposition to the Reserves has not by any means died; there are those cocoa farmers and some landowners, some politicians too, who regard the Reserves as reserves for cocoa growing. There lies calamity. Government has set its face against de-reservation and its stated policy is the maintenance, above all, of the permanent forest estate. Politics can be a hard and harsh business; no one likes to lose power, money or face, and it is within the bounds of possibility that sometime a political party may use the Reserves as bargaining counters. It may be that this will be imposed on them. Six thousand square miles of potential cocoa plantations represent the most valuable of all political weapons; a weapon that ill-used could mean a swift economic retrogression and a return to the worst features of old colonialism. The people, especially the farmers and the land-owners, must be taught this; it is not sufficient that their masters know it and appreciate it: the people make the Government; the people can unmake it and the economic nub, cocoa, could easily be the lever.

CHAPTER SIX

Managing the Forest

THE tropical high forest is so rich an association, so apparently untidy, and so vast in all directions, that the novice cannot see the wood for the trees and the problem of managing it on the sacrosanct principle of a maximum sustained yield, seems insoluble to him. It is bad enough to have to guess at the increment; almost as bad is the inability of the forester to select his calculated and chosen yield. In tidy temperate forestry, the forester having consulted his yield tables, pulls on his boots, whistles up his dog and goes out into the forest to select and mark the yield. As a practised gardener will thin a bed of lettuce, leaving it evenly spaced with those to grow on, so does the temperate forester, *mutatis mutandis*, select his yield.

The physical business of selection in the tropical forest begins with a survey. Every area of reserved forest in Ghana before it can be exploited must be stock-surveyed. There are nearly six thousand square miles (3,840,000 acres) of exploitable Reserves in Ghana; every acre has to be mapped, and every valuable tree has to be measured and numbered. With an average stocking of two mature trees per acre, the present position of some $7\frac{1}{2}$ million trees has to be plotted on the stock maps. As the scale of the maps is twenty-five inches to the mile, their plotting and preparation is a major forestry operation involving a considerable area of paper each year. Some 1,500 acres of paper will ultimately be involved not including copies.

When the stock maps are completed, they show, by coloured circles, each colour representing a different species, the location of the exploitable trees on the ground. No aerial photograph could show this because of the inter-meshing of the crowns of the trees. The Forest Officer has a clear picture of where the trees of different species and different sizes (which are also indicated) occur. He can also determine at a glance the major topographical features for this information is also surveyed and mapped. With the list of species which have been calculated to form the yield, representing the annual increment of that part of the forest, i.e., a sustained annual yield, he can quickly select them from the trees shown on the map with more silvicultural accuracy than his temperate counterpart. In the perfect normal forest which the forester has created in his mind, each tree is a normal tree, neither too greedy nor suppressed. Each has the same *lebensraum* of root and shoot; each grows regularly, evenly, straight upwards: the trade demands long straight stems.

On the ground, even in a tidy English forest, it is largely a work of art to select a good yield: to mark for felling those trees which *have* to come out, as well as those which *ought* to come out. The forester has to see in his mind's eye the forest as it will look *after* the trees he has marked have been felled and hauled out. The picture is often quite different from the one imagined. Silviculturally, without having seen the particular area of forest, but knowing nevertheless the kind of forest concerned, the tropical forester can select his yield precisely.

To the exploiter the stock-map is not only a guide to his annual cutting area, known as a coupe, it shows him where each tree he is permitted to fell stands. As each tree is deeply scribed with its serial number, there is no need for mistakes; and no excuse for them. This he knows. The Forest Ranger knows. This knowledge reduces the incidence of malpractices which, human nature being what it is, sometimes occur when yields are apportioned more haphazardly. A Technical Forest Guard with a list of the selected trees' numbers, a copy of which goes also to the contractor, follows in his wake and should ensure that no 'mistakes' have been made. Overcutting is a more serious silvicultural than moral offence.

The unit area for forest management is the *compartment*, usually about half a square mile in extent and selected as far as possible so that it cannot easily 'get lost' its boundaries being prominent natural features or permanent roads. It is a permanent unit and its history knows no ending. Every salient feature of its botany, geography and geology is recorded in the Compartment Register.

The exploiter's headaches really begin when he is allotted the yield. From that point onwards, discounting the vicissitudes he has suffered in obtaining the timber rights, he now has to spend continuously. A parcel of mahogany may be worth £1,000 delivered at Takoradi docks. A couple of inches of rain, the equivalent of two hundred tons of water per acre of forest, can immobilize his tractor and lorry fleet for a week; six inches have been known to fall in as many hours, and may cause him to 'miss the the bus'. The logs may arrive too late to be shipped, a contract is, inadvertently, broken and he may have to sell for what he can get. A small man will have to take what the brokers will give him. A larger firm can afford dock storage charges until another ship or another contract can be found.

Though the timber broker is usually an honest man, there are some who seek to flourish on the misfortunes of others. Spot cash can work wonders among men who are desperately short of money, especially if they are in debt, and there are brokers who are always at hand in the docks ready with a sheaf of notes to buy at their own price. A little man and his logs are often soon parted for a pittance; sometimes for less than it has cost him to buy the trees, fell them, cross-cut them and haul them out of the forest. A major repair to his tractor, a prolonged wet spell and he goes out of business. This is something which threatens him each year like a cold in the head. The country is full of itinerant contractors looking for easy money and rarely finding it. Rising costs, selective markets, and reduced accessibility have numbered the profitable days of the little man.

Thus the alignment of his logging roads are of primary importance. The timber exploiter is rarely a surveyor and can rarely afford to employ one. The value of a stock map is that it also shows major features, hills and valleys and streams and the exploiter, if he is literate, can roughly determine where his roads ought to go. In Reserves the alignments must be approved by the Forest Officer before a yard of road is built. This is to safeguard the exploiter as well as to make extraction as simple and as speedy as possible. A road in the wrong place is a nuisance and may make the proper working of the forest unnecessarily difficult and uneconomical. Out of the forester's necessity, and the limitations which the forest imposes on him, has thus evolved a system and a service which considerably lightens both his and our burden.

The determination of the yield which is based on the increment of the forest, which is the sum of all the increments of the mature trees, is achieved by periodic remeasurement so that the out-turn from the forest cannot exceed its growth which is thus a sustained yield. The Combined Operation, the 'brain-child' of John Mooney achieves this remeasurement by a hundred per cent enumeration combined with stock survey and improvement thinnings. This operation is new and revolutionary, and like many new and revolutionary things was received with doubt and is regarded with suspicion. It is difficult to carry out and expensive, but no more expensive than the three separate operations which it combines, and in being quicker, it is cheaper and probably more efficient in the long run. A minimum of nineteen men, including a Forest Ranger and three Forest Guards, comprises a Combined Operation party which for all practical purposes spends a year at a time entirely in the bush.

All valuable trees are measured and all over seven feet GBH are enscribed with a serial number. (GBH is Girth Breast Height, four feet three inches above the ground.) As the survey continues, the young valuable species of which there are fourteen in Class I and ten in Class II, are freed of climbers and of competition from non-valuable trees growing within twelve and six feet radii respectively. These are cut or poisoned. Any other non-valuable tree which is actually suppressing a valuable tree is also either felled or killed with arsenical poison.

The young valuables are those below five feet GBH and it is on these young *élite* that treatment is lavished because it is these which will benefit most from the improvements. Untreated, these valuable trees are expected to reach felling size in forty to sixty years. By reducing root competition and giving them more light and eliminating the strangling climbers, it is estimated that their response by increased growth will take them into the felling size class much sooner, i.e., in twenty to forty years. Most of the trees above five feet GBH already have their crowns in the uppermost canopy and treatment is unlikely to have much effect on their growth rates. Remeasurement and re-treatment cannot economically be done at an interval of less than ten years. It is not astonishing that forestry breeds patient men.

The word 'taungya' has an Oriental ring. It is derived from the Burmese word *taung* meaning hill; *ya* means cultivation, and has been developed outside Burma into a regulated system of forest farming. In areas where there is a land hunger, and as yet there are relatively few such areas in Ghana, selected farmers are given up to one acre of forest of the poorest type within a Forest Reserve and are allowed to farm it for food in return for tending a plantation of valuable trees planted in the farm by the Forestry Division. It costs about 28s an acre in labour alone to establish a *taungya* farm; of this the Local Council or the farmer pays 20s.

Like all other forestry operations conducted by the Division, the routine to be followed is detailed in the *Manual of Procedure*, MOP. This, the Ghana Forest Officer's ' bible ', comprises five bulky volumes compiled over the years in order that every major routine operation and many minor ones together with full details of financial and administrative procedure, research and management data, scales of uniforms, disciplinary action, and the form which a management, concession or working plan shall take, shall be fully understood by every executive officer.

Permits are issued to *taungya* farmers and a set of rules prescribed. The selected area is part of a larger ' Conversion ' block, for the ideal is to convert the poor, uneven-aged, untidy forest to contiguous blocks of rich, even-aged, tidy plantations. The Forest Ranger, complying with MOP demarcates and surveys the area and marks those valuable young trees which must be left standing. The remainder can be destroyed. The farmer must cut pegs four to five feet long, sufficient to cover his farm at a spacing of 16½ feet by 16½ feet. The Forest Ranger pegs the farm, whereupon the farmer may plant and sow his foodcrops. No permanent crops may be planted. When this has been done in such a way that the mature crops will not overshadow the young trees, the Ranger plants the young trees, one at each peg.

The farmer tends the trees as part of the bargain. At the end of two or three years, by which time his crops will have been gathered, his tenancy ends and he applies for a fresh area which, if he has been a good tenant, is readily granted. Not all men are honest and we have been duped often enough by farmers who affix their thumb-print to the agreement and abuse their privileges. They get no second chance if we can help it. With these exceptions the method works well and some splendid and valuable *taungya* plantations will shortly be ready for the axe.

F*

Alas, the growing of the much-wanted mahogany and Cedars has not often been a success. On the high steep slopes of the Northern Scarp Forest Reserve near the Afram Plains, these species produced pole crops fifty and more to the acre, straight round stems with high promise of a rich return. The wretched shoot-borer (*Hypsipila*), however, destroys the leading shoot year after year, debilitating the young trees and causing side-shoots to develop which result in twisted stems. Today, our new young *taungya* plantations are pure stands of *Terminalia superba*, Limba to the trade, whose wood is now appearing on some European markets. It is a swift-growing species which should be ready for the axe well within a man's lifetime. Other swift growers, such as the West Indian Cigar Box Cedar, will also be tried.

Enrichment planting and *taungya* necessitate the raising of thousands of seedlings each year. When the former is in full swing and some ten square miles are planted annually, half a million seedlings will have to be raised each year. The usual small Range nursery is being abandoned in favour of large central nurseries as communications are now such that plants can be delivered to any site within twenty-four hours.

The problem of soil fertility in permanent nurseries is one that has worried us far more than the same problem has worried the cocoa farmer who happily plucks his crop year after year, oblivious of the steady depletion of the soil's fertility and unconscious of his gradual crop diminution. The MOP details precisely how compost shall be made and applied to maintain soil fertility.

The problems of establishing plantations in the arid north and on the infertile southern plains, is one that involves land tenure as well as soil treatment. In the north where land is communally owned the question of acquisition is usually not difficult. In the more populous south, however, where ownership is usually by families and often is not clearly defined, co-operation with the people is difficult and the establishment of plantations has been delayed accordingly. Arid and infertile though the land often is, yielding neither crops nor pasture, yet the owners cling to it with the primitive tenacity which acknowledges that of all worldly things only the earth is real and immutable. In some instances plantations have been abandoned because of threats to Forest Guards (one of whom recently disappeared without trace) and wilful destruction of the young trees, thousands of which were destroyed by fire.

The current programme of establishing plantations, mainly for fuel-wood and building poles, but also including a teak *timber* plantation in the north, is about eight hundred acres per annum involving the raising of nearly 250,000 nursery plants each year. This work is concentrated mainly in the north and on the coastal plain where considerable experience of growing exotic trees has been obtained in the past decade. On the Accra Plains and further east in Trans-Volta Togoland, soils are intractable, being bone-hard in the dry season, and porridge-like in the rains. Soil analyses and the physical examination of soil structure by experts indicated that large expanses of these soils could not be expected to grow any crops. Fortunately we ignored the experts, who have so often been wrong in Ghana, and by ploughing and planting on the ridges, and by weeding, we have succeeded in growing trees, mostly exotics, better than in most high forest areas, suggesting that soil structure is more important to a tree's roots than all the nutrients in Africa. Height growths of up to fifteen feet have been commonly achieved in two years and it is hoped that results such as these can be maintained over a rotation. If they can, the problem of the afforestation of a thousand square miles of semi-desert is solved.

Whether the Division of Forestry should continue to battle with local inhabitants often no less intractable than the soils which they cherish, or whether the local people themselves should be educated to an appreciation of the necessity for afforestation in tree-less areas, and exhorted to do their own tree-planting, is now being decided. Extension work, as it is called, is being undertaken with the latter end in view. The policy of the Ministry of Agriculture is to encourage the people of the plains themselves to grow wood-lots and small plantations, thereby minimizing land 'palavers' and allowing the Division of Forestry more opportunity to manage the forest estate.

Whether extension work will succeed is a moot point. The Ghanaian is a strong individualist and is not easily persuaded to work for something that cannot demonstrably be proved to be immediately profitable. He is not inclined to socialism and likes to make his own decisions and guide his own plough, primitive though that may be. The ideal of each family establishing its own permanent wood-lot and enjoying, in perpetuity, the benefits of its shade, enhanced soil fertility, protection from harsh winds, ample fuel and building materials, even with considerable assistance from the Government, is an ideal of which I think the people not yet worthy.

CHAPTER SEVEN

On Trek in the Banda

WE reached the Banda Hills with little incident. The car caught fire on the Wenchi road and I had to spend the night on the roadside, which was no hardship. A case of four dozen bottles of beer which had gone on ahead by carrier and was to provide my evening comfort for two weeks was *dropped* and six bottles smashed. Kodjo-the-cook had left my mosquito net behind and I had to use his (one of my old ones) which was full of large holes. Finally, we got stuck in floods near Menji.

Of all these incidents, the car-fire was the most spectacular. The car was a Ford V-8 tourer which I had recently (1946) bought for £70. This was what Burra, ACF, had paid me for the 'Cocoa Bean'. another Ford which saw much service with various Forest Officers in her remarkable twenty years life. Ford cars have served me well throughout most of my Colonial Service and I cannot blame Mr Ford for the slight trouble I had with the V-8. She had 31,000 miles on the clock when I bought her, hammered out of her on laterite roads little better than cart tracks in more civilized countries

The V-8 suffered from thirst which, like her owner's, could never be assuaged. Her lack, however, was petrol, and the day before the Banda trek I had cleaned out the petrol feed system. Where the petrol feed pipe entered the carburettor was a tiny steel pyramidical valve. This fitted in the pipe and stopped the further entry of petrol when the carburettor was full. Without it the petrol pump would continue to flood the carburettor with results that can be imagined and will be described. I removed this valve and placed it on the cylinder head.

We set out from Sunyani, the District headquarters, in mid-afternoon the following day, laden to full capacity. Robert the Corgi stood happily on the high-piled loads in the open back drinking the breeze as we roared and clattered our way northwards on the Wenchi road now corrugated like an enlarged wash-board. At anything under forty mph it was like driving a wheelbarrow over a corrugated iron roof. Therefore we kept well above that speed.

At some time in its geological history, a considerable area of Ghana seems to have been squeezed laterally resulting in a seem-ingly endless series of steep ridges and depressions. The Sunyani-Wenchi road traverses one of these series. In the deep valleys, the culverts were of two-inch planks laid flat on the road. Thus the end of the planks stood up above the road surface. I did not realize this until we hit one with the impetus derived from an overladen motor car free-wheeling at the bottom end of a long steep slope. With petrol in short supply I copied the dangerous practice of the 'mammy' lorry drivers and switched off at the top of a hill. The impact lifted the car off its four wheels and sent Robert curving in a gentle arc over my head, over the bonnet, into the right-hand ditch! The car came down with a frightening crash of glass from the back, but did not disintegrate. We pulled up and recovered an astonished but unhurt dog, did a swift inspection of the car and went on more circumspectly.

A little way on I began to feel uncomfortably hot, especially about the feet and legs, as though the engine was overheating. Glancing down I was astonished to see flames licking at the floor-board. I stopped the car as smartly as I could and Robert went overboard a second time, this time not without loud remonstrance. Kodjo and I were out of the car almost as speedily. I flung up the bonnet to be rewarded by leaping flames and black smoke. 'Get dirty,' I yelled. This was an injunction to gather soil, known throughout West Africa as 'dirty'. We scrabbled with our bare hands at the red pebbly laterite on the roadside and flung the stuff into the conflagration. We got the flames out without the explo-sion which I feared and without any vital damage which I could see. The cylinder block was almost red-hot and there was a sicken-ing stench of burnt rubber and oil.

The cause of the fire was still sitting on the cylinder head where I had placed it, which was a great slice of luck for without the tiny steel pyramidical valve there would have been a different story to tell. I had forgotten to replace it and consequently petrol had been pumped into the carburettor faster than the engine could use it.

The surplus must have been forced out as a spray which so long as the engine was cool was harmless. As soon as the engine really warmed up it ignited.

It would be hours before the engine was cool enough to touch so that we could clean the grit out of the carburettor and replace the valve. It was then late afternoon and there was nothing to do but stay the night. Kodjo unpacked the car and put up my camp bed, table and chair, I had an early dinner out of tins cooked on the roadside and went to bed with Robert underneath, and Kodjo in the back of the car. It was at this point that Kodjo discovered that he had forgotten my second net and so I used his. Thus I shortly afterwards suffered my second dose of malaria. No lorry or car passed us during all this time and we had had breakfast and cleaned up the car, replaced the valve and were on our way again an hour after dawn the next day.

At Menji, which we passed three hours later, all being well, we left the proper (*sic*) road and turned north into the Banda country, travelling now on a rough track that was washed away annually and roughly re-made when the rains had passed. It was thick with silver sand, rich in pot-holes, water-holes and mud swamps. Down the middle the grass grew radiator high and hid heaven knew what hazards. I kept in second gear and ground a hesitant way along it.

The people of the Banda country, though it lies in north-west Ashanti separated from the northern tribes by the great Volta River, are not Ashantis. Their affinities lie in the north with the Mohammedan peoples and like them they are cattle raisers. The Banda country is characterized by the prominent Banda Hills, some of them mountain peaks extending up to 2,000 feet. The vegetation is largely *savannah* with closed forest along the rivers. In the dry season it is blackened with fire, excessively hot and dusty. In the rains, the extensive grassy plains and the numerous streams, dry for most of the year, are flooded. The Tembe and Wewa streams rising in the hills become raging torrents and man-sized boulders move like living things along the stream-beds, driven by the furious water. The hills themselves form a watershed several hundred square miles in extent and an inch or two of rain, which sometimes falls in a few minutes, fills the dry, quiet beds with a roaring that sounds like thunder. Bridges and tracks disappear regularly each year.

A few miles north of Menji we struck floods. I sent Kodjo ahead to see whether the water was too deep to drive through. At no point did it cover his knees so I decided to try it. At too slow a speed we should certainly stick; too fast and we might skid and turn over. I went in in second gear and all went well till about half-way when we struck an extra slimy patch of submerged mud, skidded and stopped. Further tractive efforts merely dug the rear wheels deeper: I switched off wondering if we should have to spend a night there, and surveyed the scene.

Ahead, to the north, rose the Banda Hills, cone-shaped many of them, their dry brown flanks sharp against the cloudless blue. The straight line of road ran ahead for miles, disappearing into the cluster of hills where lay our destination, the resthouse in Banda village. The sooner we began to walk the sooner we would arrive. No help was likely; we had passed no one on the way and it was not likely that we should see anyone till we hit the next village, Sabiya. There I might be able to persuade a few boys to help me to push the car out. I sat and smoked a cigarette while Robert, as always with untroubled mind, certain of his next meal and satisfied with any place near me for a bed, explored the low, open *savannah* forest which was so pleasant a change from the high dark forest further south. There was no shade; the sun was almost vertically above; it was too hot to think, let alone walk to Sabiya.

Suddenly a bush-fowl cackled, exploded from the grass and with a flurry of wings came low and fast over the car. Robert, like a rusty red-legged sausage, was off at once in hot pursuit. I watched the bird crash noisily into a Shea Butter tree and sit there watching the dog. I collected my ·22 rifle from the back of the car, checked the few rounds of ammunition in my blouse pocket, opened the car door and waded after the dog.

For a Corgi with a touch of dachshund in him, Robert was a remarkably good and patient pointer. I knew I would find him beneath the tree, his long muzzle pointed at the bush-fowl, slavering a little, his tail swishing noisily among the leaves. Not that I needed a pointer in this case, for the bird imagined that if he kept still he could not be seen, and though the few strap-like leaves of the Shea Butter tree gave him some protection he was plainly visible fifty yards away. I shot him from twenty yards whereupon Robert lost interest. Dead animals held no fascination for him, though he would enjoy my leavings. During our years together we co-operated in the despatch of hundreds of bush-fowl and green pigeon; he did the chasing and pointing, I effected the kill. As far as I was concerned it was not sport, but it provided exercise for us both and a well filled pot. Robert at home was a gentle, affectionate, gentlemanly dog. In bush, whether high or low, he rampaged the whole day through, savouring Heaven knows what canine delights. If there is a Heaven for dogs I know that Robert will have asked for nothing more than a limitless expanse of celestial bush.

The bush-fowl presaged another slice of good luck. Three Baza-barima boys bound for the north, their meagre possessions slung from their shoulders, appeared suddenly from the bush and did not hesitate to help us when Kodjo, who knew their tongue, asked them to help to push the car out of the lake. With the aid of the engine, judiciously applied in bottom gear with much slipping of the clutch, Kodjo and the Bazabarimas pushing, we got on to dry ground again. They received a shilling each which they accepted with a polite smile and followed slowly in our wake as we ground gently in second gear towards Banda.

At Sabiya we caught up with the carriers and discovered that the bridge over the Tombe was down and that we should have to walk to Banda. I decided to press on. The carriers hastily built a leaf-roofed shelter for the car, hoisted their loads and we set off in the full blast of the afternoon sun. We reached the Banda Rest-house as dusk was falling and I had long savoured the delicious anticipation of a bottle of beer. Hot, fizzy and bitter.

The resthouse was a barn-like structure with a thatch roof, no doors or windows, just openings in the swish walls, and inhabited by sweat bees, mason wasps and cows. The former had no lack of sweat when I moved in and shooed the latter off the shady verandah. All the carriers but one, who acted as cook's mate whether he liked it or not, moved off into Banda as happy as if they owned the earth. I do not suppose the ten of them could raise a florin between them. No matter, a traveller in Africa must be housed and fed, and if necessary bedded down with a woman. It was dark before the cook's mate had heated my bath water, by which time I had quenched my thirst and by the light of the pres-sure lamp had glanced through some of the latest batch of papers, nearly two months old. Kodjo meanwhile had put up the bed and prepared dinner.

It was after my bath when I had mellowed somewhat and was anticipating a substantial meal that he reported the six bottles of beer smashed. That was the worst thing that had happened to me so far.

Banda Resthouse lies on the edge of an extensive plain at the foot of the hills. Almost from the compound itself one of them rose 1,200 feet in little over a mile. It was cool in the evening and a delightful change from the cloying claustrophobic heat of the forest, and it cannot have been much later than 7 pm when I climbed gratefully into the net-draped camp bed, which my sons still use occasionally when unexpected guests arrive. The state of the net augured ill for me if there were many mosquitoes. But I was too tired to care.

Hours later I needed to visit the small room, and fumbling my way, half-asleep, in the pitch darkness, I fell over something large, soft and warm and certainly alive! For a moment I was terrified, till reason told me that no lion had descended from the hills, but that the cows had returned. Nor did they seem to mind as I clambered over their backs to and from the latrine. There is always something happening in Africa; no two days are ever alike.

We were up with the dawn and after a substantial breakfast, during which time the carriers arrived and began to repack those loads which had been opened, I set up the prismatic compass on its stand and centred it over the survey pillar which stood conveniently a few hundred yards from the resthouse. By this time, Forest Ranger Bonnie-Apiagye had arrived with his labourers. We were the team which were beginning the demarcation of the Banda Watershed Forest Reserve. The carriers were going ahead to make camp on the hill-top while we cut and surveyed a tie-line from the pillar, up the flank of the hill to a suitable point from whence we could cut and survey a line around the Banda Hills. It was an exciting moment. The hills were mine for the next few months while I placed a line, a man-made halter, as it were, around their vast, aloof fastnesses. No one lived there but the wild beasts; who knows what we should find? I had made a rough outline on the field sheet indicating where I thought the line should run; topography would probably modify this as we explored this almost unknown territory. I could not know it then, but three years work was necessary before the demarcation was completed.

The labourers began cutting the tall dew-drenched grass along a sighting between tall poles set on a compass bearing. I read off the bearings, the Forest Ranger booked them and the distances in ten-chain units as the chain gang laid the chain along the line. The leading chain man had ten 'arrows' and as each chain was laid he stuck one carefully into the ground adjacent to the brass handle of the chain. As the chain was moved along the line the end chain man collected the arrow. When he had collected ten arrows he called 'ten chains', the Ranger counted the arrows and recorded the distance in his field book and the process was repeated. One hundred chains from our starting point I ended the tie-line. We drove in the first wooden boundary pillar and marked it 'FRBP I', Forest Reserve Boundary Pillar No. I; later all the wooden pillars would be replaced by concrete ones. From FRBP I, I sighted the first leg of the new Reserve northwards towards the Volta River.

The main object of reservation was to protect the headwaters of the numerous streams which rise in the hills and water a thousand square miles of land and upon which the people and cattle of Banda depend. The hills themselves, a hundred and fifty square miles of them, extend in a great mass west of Banda village to the frontier with the Ivory Coast. It was full of game, including lion, leopard and elephant, but few people went there for it was too remote and was the reputed haunt of numerous spirits. A few hunters dared the remoteness of its lonely scarps, but only for a few weeks in the year. The appalling, often non-existent roads from the south leading to Banda kept out the Syrian and Lebanese element and the only way in from the north was across the wide Volta and by footpath to Banda. It was not an area to attract the kind of expatriate and African hunter who has in the past decade decimated the game in northern Ghana and has wiped out most of the game in Banda. To preserve the headwaters meant to preserve the vegetation on the hills, keep out fire and the farmer's hoe. The Reserve was made just in time, for recent years have seen a great extension in agriculture and an increase in population. The destruction of the vegetation on the hills would have destroyed the headwaters, denied water to the people of the plains and prevented any major agricultural development.

When rain falls in this locality it often falls with great violence. Clouds mass above the peaks, lightning flashes and its thunder resounds and reverberates with unusual fury, being flung from one peak to another in a long series of explosions which torture the eardrums. Dry hair crackles with static. The wind rises to gale force within seconds and furious gusts threaten the tents and fill the air with grit and dust. Then the rain sluices down quenching the wind in one violent spasm. Small dry runnels fill instantly and become tiny torrents; small streams fill more slowly but within minutes are raging with brown water; the larger streams may take an hour or so to run free.

Without a dense vegetative cover, rain of such violence, even though it is often only a few minutes' duration, can desecrate the soil, sweeping away its valuable topsoil, carving the naked earth into gullies which will deepen year by year until nature refuses to reclaim them, and denying the underground reservoirs the water which maintains the perennial streams and wells: the rain simply runs off the earth's surface and is lost.

We had no rain. The sky remained cloudless and the sun blared down on us ceaselessly from dawn till about 5 pm when it dipped behind the hills. It was easily bearable until about 10 am. From then on we roasted and choked in the dust generated by the slashing cutlasses. Forest Guard Obeng acted as my orderly, carrying my ·22 rifle and a haversack containing two bottles of boiled and filtered water. The labourers hacked away, scarcely pausing to rest, shining with sweat and coated with red dust. Towards noon even they donned vests as protection against the sun. Robert found himself a little patch of shade and lay there panting while the work proceeded for two or three chains. He then caught us up and sought another shady spot. The sweat bees, real bees in miniature, fortunately stingless, sought the sweat about our eyes; the tsetse flies patrolled and darted in and out, biting; Simulium flies, carriers of the dreaded River Blindness, bit us till they fell off with the weight of blood.

The bearing ran a few degrees east of north most of the way. Periodically it was necessary to scout ahead and reconnoitre the terrain. I wanted long straight 'legs' as they are more economical to cut and to maintain than a lot of 'dogs' legs'. Where it seemed likely that we would hit a cliff face or a scree I altered the bearing for the time being but maintained our northerly direction. At the rate of a mile and a half a day we hacked our way towards the Volta River. This was a contrast with life in the forest and after a few days of it, I wished myself a hundred miles south. I have always thought sunbathing a useless pursuit, with no benefits in it and little pleasure. Handsome men may be 'slightly sunburnt' but the baking which they must suffer to achieve this apparently desirable result, must be purgatory. But for us there was no escape from the sun until 5 pm, by which time we had usually returned to camp and were lying in the deepest patch of shade available, soaking up filter water by the quart and scratching our bites. After a week I was almost indistinguishable from the rest.

The first couple of nights in camp I was exhausted and slept heavily, dead to the world. Even lions roaring close by the camp, the boys told me, did not awaken me. A lion's roaring in a Zoo is an awe-inspiring noise for a little while, after which it becomes irritating. A lion roaring in earnest in his native habitat makes one's hair stand on end if one is within a quarter of a mile of him. It has a rare ventriloquial property and this allied to the topography of the Banda lent it some added qualities.

A lion killed that night a mile or so from my tent. I awoke to hear it roaring. The sound, great shuddering waves of it, seemed to come from all directions as though we were ringed with roaring lions. My scalp tingled and the hair crawled up the back of my neck; Robert, beneath my bed, 'sang', a noise he usually made when I played my piano accordion. This cacophany went on for half an hour and I was like a wet rag when it ceased and I could hear again the friendly stridulation of the grasshoppers and crickets.

We visited the scene of the kill a few days later on my way back to Sunyani. The lion had killed a fine water-buck, with a magnificent spread of twenty-four inches across his curving horns. The villagers of Bui nearby had set a man-trap for the lion, a great steel contraption with wicked teeth, made from old lorry springs. It had a gape wide enough to take an elephant. This they had chained to a stout log among the remains of the kill. They 'bagged' a leopard with it. From my camp bed I heard the screams of the big cat on the night following the kill, and silence, but did not know the circumstances. The leopard rampaged most of the night, they told me, but no one thought of going near it, trapped as it was. A lion is a beast to command every respect, but hell hath no fury like an angry leopard. At dawn a hunter shot it and put it out of its misery.

The horns of the water-buck now hang in my home near Taunton in Somerset; the leopard's skin which I bought, I kept for years until the leather beetles got at it and ruined it. I have often wondered whether the lion I met one morning early after breakfast, was the one that killed and woke me with its triumphant roaring. It was near Bui, the day we hit the Volta River; the day we were routed by hornets; the day Forest Guard Obeng nearly died.

The labourers, led by the Ranger, had gone ahead while I enjoyed my breakfast, warmly clad in a thick sweater, savouring the comparative cold of an early morning in the hills. Those mornings, shortly after dawn, when the sun was still an invisible threat, after a deep sleep which the sodden forest in the south so often denied me, were a delight. The air was cold and dry and a man could breathe; his pores could close; his mind and body had a chance to relax.

With Forest Guard Obeng carrying the haversack and rifle, I followed in the wake of the others; it was my last day in the Banda. After we had hit the river, the Ranger would carry on. Life at that moment was good: I had enjoyed my breakfast, the coffee had been good and hot and strong, I was young, healthy, with no cares, and tomorrow I returned to comparative civilization. I had earned a respite and I could go back to play poker with Ian Cameron and Vernon Littlewood.

I had some such thoughts in my mind as I marched through the *savannah* forest, hearing the cackle of bush fowl and the soft beat of a tambourine dove, when I met the lion. He was as big as a donkey. I halted, my mind in a panic, but not so much of a panic that I wanted to run, only wishing the ground would swallow me up, at once. I smelled lion: the unmistakable acid reek of cat. He looked at me with a yellow, speculative eye. His nose was black and as big as my fist; his paws were enormous; I could visualize the sheathed claws. He yawned, doubtless to exhibit his magnificent fangs. I was relieved to note that his tail, that quite unmajestic appendage, was not swishing its black hairy tip from side to side, a sign, I had always read, of anger and impending charge. He licked his left fore paw, the one nearest me, and I could hear the rasp of his tongue like a file on wood, gave me another quick glance from his large, yellow eye and moved on. I stood, petrified, watching him as he disappeared, noiselessly. The tambourine dove still beat its mournful refrain; cicadas screamed and I heard my own breathing. It was something to be breathing.

The Forest Guard summed it up when a little later I enquired of his sensations. 'Sir,' he said, 'I think heaven and earth be one.' We agreed it had been a moving experience. I remember, sixteen years afterwards, that there were seven long black-tipped hairs on the left cheek of the lion's jaw!

As we gradually drew near the river, the vegetation began to thicken and soon we were fighting our way through a mixture of scrub and high forest in places liberally laced with wait-a-bit thorns. There were numerous old signs of elephant and bush cow and the spoor of numerous antelope were evident about the water holes, now dry. The web-shaped marks left by the feet of crocodile were occasionally imprinted in the rock-hard soil. For many years the Volta had flooded its banks at the height of the rains and there was ample evidence of successive flooding in the thick deposit of silt, now as hard as rock, and the dead remains of trees torn from the banks and left when the waters receded.

We were within half a mile of the river when the tsetse flies and Simulium flies suddenly increased in number. The species of tsetse which attack us, breeds in shaded soil near water, while the Simulium lays its eggs in thin transparent straps in running water; there was plenty of that. The lack of game at this time of year had starved them and we suffered cruelly. We slew these carriers of sleeping sickness and river blindness by the thousand and still they came on swift silent wings. As a soldier in war becomes battle-hardened to the point where he no longer fears death or mutilation, so years of proximity to the vast catalogue of insect-borne diseases had bred in me an indifference to them. No one could be indifferent to the immediate effects of their bites, however, and the irritation they caused was considerable. I scratched even in my sleep, and it says much for the constitution which my forefathers handed on to me that in over twenty years of bites by every imaginable fly, numbering countless thousands of punctures by disease and dirt-carrying insects, only once did I suffer any infection from the bite itself.

We speak and write of 'bites', but these insects *suck* our blood: Mosquitoes (including the malaria- and yellow-fever-carrying types), Tsetses (some of which confer sleeping sickness), Simulium (the vector of Onchocerciasis or river blindness), Culicine 'sand-flies' which give a 'break-bone' fever, very much like sandfly fever, numerous *Haematopota*, Mango flies (which can transmit Filariasis), and the almost miscroscopic 'Fire' fly, which I discovered at Ammumuniso. None of these bite with jaws, because they have none. They all employ a hypodermic system, usually quite painless in its action. The irritation which arises afterwards is apparently due to an injection by the insect of a salivary fluid which may contain the agents of disease: the plasmodia of malaria; the undulating trypanosomes of sleeping sickness; the miscroscopic worms of Filariasis. The irritation is caused by an anti-coagulant, which allows the insect to suck blood unimpeded by blood clots.

We could hear the murmur of the river long before we saw it. It would be our first glimpse of running water in two weeks; I vowed I would swim, bilharzia or no. I sent Forest Guard Obeng on ahead, leaving the rifle and haversack behind, which as events transpired was just as well. 'When you reach the river bank, shout!' I told him. We would take the last bearing of this leg on his voice. Obeng disappeared and we waited, trying to rest while doing constant battle with the flies.

Five minutes had passed when there came a faint cry. I began to 'sight' the compass on it. In the quiet forest it is possible to take an accurate bearing on a distant voice. The labourers stirred, uneasily I thought. The cry came again. 'What does he say?' I asked. They answered, 'Mewu, mewu.' It took a second or two to penetrate. 'Run,' I cried. They were already running. We ran like hounds towards the cries. No need to take a bearing. *Mewu* means 'I am dying'.

What, I thought, could it be? A snake, leopard, crocodile? It was none of these things. Obeng had fallen into a mud-hole and when we appeared the mud was almost up to his chin. There was terror in the man's face, his eyes protruded. He was inches and seconds from death and he knew it. We drew him from the liquid mud, which relinquished him reluctantly with beastly, sucking sounds as though some slimy reptile were protesting at being cheated of its prey.

Then it became a joke! With death behind them everybody began to laugh; the labourers rolled on the ground choking with laughter. The Forest Ranger smote his knee with joy; Robert barked and pretended to bite everyone; two minutes after being hauled out even the slime-covered Obeng laughed. 'Mewu, mewu,' mimicked the labourers, and laughed again. Death had been cheated; that was something to laugh about. Years after, Obeng, now a Senior Forest Guard, grins when I chide him with 'Mewu'.

We sighted and measured the last leg of the eastern boundary. Standing on the south bank of the Volta River, Ranger Apiagye closed the field book with date and signature; I checked the running total. After a hasty dip in the river, for it was running strongly and there were crocodiles about, and also bilharzia is an unpleasant disease, we turned back to camp.

Nature had not finished with us yet. On our return, someone disturbed a nest of hornets and we were scattered to the four points of the compass! No one escaped and so swollen and distorted were some the carriers' faces that they were unrecognizable. They looked like men from another world. It was a night of misery, lightened for me because I was leaving the Banda on the morrow, leaving it at least a stone in weight lighter, several shades darker in hue, back to the company of my own kind. It was a feeling such as one had on the eve of one's leave, packed and ready for the mail boat.

It was a Friday night and I tuned in on my radio to Tommy Handley and ITMA. The little Eddystone battery set in its nest of old newspapers, packed into a battered Revelation suitcase, picked up London, 4,000 miles away, loud and clear. After ITMA, as I was casting around the dial for some lively music, a leopard began its grating note somewhere in the bush not far away. Another joined in and soon they began quarrelling as tom cats will quarrel on English roof-tops though several decibels louder. I tuned the reaction and made the set scream and howl. Such sounds neither they nor any other creature in the Banda can ever have heard before. They promptly shut up and I did not hear them again. The following day our return to Sunyani was without incident.

Two months later I was back again to check Apiagye's progress. Having done so I parted company with him and decided to cut part of the boundary south of Banda, an awkward leg with many changes of direction, all hugging the steep sides of hills. Soon we were lost!

My camp was near the village of Samba, a mile east of the line and as we were cutting southward I instructed Kodjo to move camp to Wewa, four miles south on the hammock path. The path ran parallel with my proposed boundary and within a couple of miles of it and I expected that by afternoon we would have cut about half the boundary towards Wewa. I took half the carriers and left the other half with Kodjo to move camp. We cut steadily through grass and scrub and patches of high forest along dry stream beds, and could only have been a couple of miles from Wewa when I called a halt for the day. The safest plan would then have been to retrace our steps to Samba and follow the hammock path to Wewa.

We were all tired, it was mid-afternoon and we had been on our feet with few pauses for eight or nine hours. The carriers had had no food or water in that time: would it not be quicker to march through the bush direct to Wewa? I asked myself the question as I studied the map. It was not far and with luck it would save us a couple of hours walking time. According to the map we should be close to the Wewa stream, a tributary of the Tombe, and my proposed line should hit it shortly. I decided that we would take the short cut and go through the bush. We walked due south on a compass bearing and within half an hour had hit the stream, with water in it. We washed and the carriers and Robert drank, and then tried to walk in the stream itself which I knew flowed close to Wewa. After several of the carriers had disappeared momentarily into deep-filled pot-holes, however, we abandoned that exercise and on another compass bearing aimed due east. Within a little more than a mile we must hit the Samba—Wewa hammock path. We hit the path as scheduled and turned right to Wewa happily, anticipating a meal within the hour.

After half an hour's swift march, our tiredness and hunger forgotten, I noticed that the wide hammock path had narrowed appreciably. This was inexplicable; if we were approaching a village it must surely widen, while farms would be evident and people. According to my reckoning we could not be more than half a mile from the village. As we slogged on, however, the path narrowed further and finally disappeared into an abandoned farm. This accounted for the lack of people; we were in a dead end, a *cul-de-sac* of bush.

I again studied the map. From it there was only one hammock path, only one path within miles of where we were supposed to be. However inconceivable it seemed that we were not on this path, it was obvious that we were not. I assumed that we must have missed a turning and had side-tracked ourselves into this miserable position. How far back the turning was we would have to find out for ourselves and in a hurry if we were to see Wewa before dark. We turned round, all eyes skinned. We were lost without that turning. Our position was not desperate, but merely unpleasant. It was now, as far as I could judge from the sun's angle, about 4 pm. We had two hours to get to Wewa, otherwise it meant a night in the bush without food or shelter; water we could get from the river, assuming we could find it again. I noted that it was strange that we had not encountered the Wewa stream again, for our general direction, which I had repeatedly checked, had been at right angles to it and converging upon it.

We investigated several side-turnings but none of them were major ones and we did not bother to pursue them. I felt dreadful. My two bottles of water had evaporated long since and I felt dehydrated, light-headed and leaden-booted. The carriers were silent, and that was a sure sign of misery.

I was near despair, the light was fast going, and it seemed as though we must surely be stuck in the bush in most unpleasant circumstances, when someone by chance found the turning on to the main path. It must have been so, judging from the ankle-thick dust on it, the sign of much bare-footed traffic. With hearts and feet considerably lighter we turned right again. Our spirits remained uplifted when we passed an old woman tottering beneath a vast head-load of firewood. Asked where she was going she answered 'Wewa'. Asked 'How far?', she replied 'No far'. But I was not being 'had'. Bitter experience had taught me that such African expressions as 'far small', and 'no far', were merely expressions of politeness to encourage the weary traveller. Time and distance mean little in the bush and twenty miles a day was nothing for even a grandmother. I doubted whether she had the slightest idea how far Wewa lay ahead!

The carriers chattered and laughed now and I lifted my blistered feet and aching knees with a little less effort. Robert's tongue by now was almost lolling in the dust, but there was no doubt at all that if I could keep going on he could. Darkness fell and still we plodded on. The taste in my mouth was bitter as gall, and I was conscious of my tongue, the swelling of which precedes acute dehydration. Suddenly a blinding light came out of the darkness, voices were raised, Robert was barking and the incredible delicious savour of cooked steak greeted us!

I have often eulogized Kodjo-the-cook. He served me well and selflessly for many years, but never so well and selflessly as on this occasion. He and the other carriers had come to meet us, on the assumption that we would not be such fools as to be far away at nightfall, with beer, a cooked dinner, table, chair, light and my pullover. The inimitable Jeeves could have done no better. The pressure lamp was slung from the low branch of a tree, I pulled my chair up to the table, quaffed the beer from my battered pewter tankard, and ate Heinz' Steak and Kidney pudding, baked jacket potatoes and green peas, straddling the hammock path from Samba to Wewa. The relief carriers, squatting around on their heels, passed noisy, good-natured, but uncomplimentary, comments on our performance, while a bush-baby chattered its descending notes nearby. My companions had continued on their way to Wewa. In a little time, after Robert had cleaned my plate, satiated and unsteady on my pins with a gross meal floating on beer inside me, I followed them. It was an occasion I cannot forget.

CHAPTER EIGHT

Up Dome Hill

THE Juaso Forestry Bungalow, perched high on the side of a hill, overlooks a thousand square miles of forest. From the long verandah the eye can roam over the vast mult-hued canopy of trees, to the horizon. On the right, to the north on the horizon, the Bandai Hills rise in smoky blue loftiness, ranging almost unbroken to their culmination a hundred and fifty miles away in the Banda Hills, tucked in the north-western corner of Ashanti. On the left, framed by the flame-flowered Poinciana trees which exult around the bungalow, is the smooth fat brow of Dome Hill. It *looks* smooth and so close that one might almost be able to touch it. If it had not been for the accursed sandflies and their bites I would have spent many more hours watching this scene ever-changing as clouds marched above throwing infinite moving patterns on to the forest roof, changing as the sun wheeled across the sky.

The District Commissioner, H. E. Devaux, had a theory about these minute blood-thirsty beasts. They bred, he maintained, in the dead leaf-axils of the oil palms among the damp detritus. Between Devaux's bungalow and mine, the only two bungalows in the Juaso station, there were scores of oil palms. We began steadily to remove the palms, ostensibly to control the sandflies, but actually to obtain the luscious palm 'cabbage' which is the sweet nutritious growing point of the palm, its heart as it were. Pluck it out and the plant dies. I did not agree with Devaux about the breeding sites of the sandflies, but as he provided the labour to fell the palms, I offered my disagreement *sotto voce*.

I was no gardener in those days and although Devaux, like all District Commissioners, had station carriers and a garden-boy to do his bidding, I cannot recall much garden produce ever coming my way, either in Juaso or any other station. The carriers harked back to the days when District Commissioners travelled around their Districts on foot, which is the only way in which one can expect to meet and understand the people. By this time (1940), the limit of a District Commissioner's trekking was the end of the motor road, plus one grand trek across the Afram Plains, once a tour, undertaken more as a shaking-up of the liver, constricted after its eighteen months' cramp at his desk and on his magisterial bench. We Forest Officers could not persuade the Government to provide us even with a watchman for our bungalows during the weeks we were 'bush-whacking'; for years I was my own messenger and cleaner in the office. Understandably we were critical of the over-staffed District Commissioners.

Devaux was not far wrong in his theory about the breeding habits of the sandfly. That he could not have been absolutely right was obvious from the fact that sandflies bred in their millions in the deep forest where there were no palm-trees. It has since been established that these tiny mosquitoes do breed in the damp leafy detritus, such as may be found in the old leaf axils of palm trees, or indeed, anywhere where there is an abundance of moist, easily accessible, slowly decaying vegetation. Today, the sandfly menace at Juaso is considerably lessened, but that is probably due to the general clearance of all the bush from the station area. In my day, leopard roamed the forest just above my bungalow.

Over the fat hump of Dome Hill ran the northern boundary of Dome Hill Forest Reserve. No senior officer had inspected this area for some years so I decided it was time someone ascertained if it was still there, and in the condition periodically reported by the Forest Guard in whose beat it lay. The carriers awoke me with their chatter and laughter while it was still half-light. How these boys (some were approaching middle-age but they were still 'boys') kept cheerful and retained a lively sense of humour even in the most trying circumstances constantly amazed me. Poor to the point of poverty, lacking any possessions other than a few rags in which they worked, and a 'best' cover cloth, and unable to afford a wife, they were constantly close to destitution. They lived together in Juaso New Town in riotous squalor. They worked according to the whim of their employer, myself, for two to three weeks a month for one shilling a day, and for the remainder of the month for anyone who would employ them. A wage of thirty shillings a month was the most they could expect to earn and even in pre-war days that did not go very far.

Most of the carriers suffered constantly from malaria, all had
worms of one kind and another, a few had yaws and without
exception they were underfed, subsisting largely on yams and cassava, starchy foods which gave them pot-bellies and yet sustained
them on marches so rigorous that I, young, healthy and superbly
fed, sometimes felt exhausted. I carried nothing but the clothes on
my back, and yet I often slumped my aching body into a camp
chair at the end of a day's trek, a chair that had been carried by
one of the carriers, while they had staggered for eight hours
through the heat of the day beneath sixty-pound loads (heavier if
it had rained) with nothing in their bellies but a handful of garri
and a cola nut! They cleaned a camp site for me, put up the tent,
collected firewood, drew water for my bath and then, only then,
attended to their own miserable comforts. Looking back I am
ashamed that I had so much and they so little, accepting this as
the natural and proper order of things.

There was never a day that one or more carriers did not turn up
for medical attention. Constipation was their worst trouble. Two
tablets of camomile chewed thoroughly not only sufficed but did
so to the accompaniment of such a horrible taste that they were
delighted. The more potent the medicine seemed, the more potent
it must be, so they reasoned. They regarded chocolate covered laxa-
tives as an opium smoker regards aspirin. They enjoyed a tablet
of quinine, convinced that chewing it made it more potent than
merely to swallow it whole. Iodine they preferred to the modern
antiseptics because it hurt them more, *ergo* it was more efficacious!
A hot bread poultice was preferred to a simple fomentation for the
same reason, and in this they were right. They loved aspirin tablets
and laughed at simple incisions. In spite of all their aches and
pains, sudden fevers and, I have no doubt, a high incidence of
venereal disease, they were always willing workers and cheerful
companions.

I remember most of their names: Tinga, Tampuri, Bambila,
Musa, 'Dogo' Baz, John Toe, Awuni and Amadu. Perhaps the
best of them all was Kodjo-the-cook; he had lost none of the
strength of his carrier days and I have seen him contemptuously
relieve a tired carrier of his load and carry it with ridiculous ease
till the end of the day, in addition to my heavy pressure lamp, his
haversack and my own. I got to know these boys better than I knew

my brother. They were ragged companions, grateful for a cigarette end, from which each would take a deep drag and pass it on until it was entirely smoked, the last boy invariably burning his thick rubbery lips and joining in the laughter at his own discomfiture. Yet never once did they beg a cigarette. While I sat in my camp chair guzzling water, there would always be a volunteer to unlace my shoes and remove them from my aching feet; to remove each individual grass awn which my stockings collected by the hundred and pricked like needles. (These belong to a common grass *Streptogyne crinita* and are pushed in masses into mouse holes to catch the mice, who are caught by the numerous recurved prickles.)

I ate my breakfast while superintending the loading; this expedited our departure and also kept the voracious sandflies at bay. The regular carriers had their regular loads. Dogo Baz, the tallest and strongest, always carried my tin bath, not because it was an easy load but because it was acknowledged to be the heaviest by far. He was a proud young man. The bath contained my typewriter and piano accordion. I reckoned to spend every Sunday morning writing, a habit which I tried to maintain for many years, and most evenings I exercised the 'squeeze box', much to Robert the Corgi's annoyance. In the rains, the tent loads could become the heaviest, as the canvas soaked up water and almost doubled in weight. These were non-regular loads. No one particularly wanted them. Chop-boxes were for the regulars. These contained tinned goods which I ate steadily thereby reducing their weight considerably. The cook's box containing his pots and pans and his meagre personal effects was also a load much in demand. The bedding bag, containing bed, linen, blankets, and net, was a long, awkward sausage-shaped contrivance and not much liked. Chop-boxes whether steady in weight or not were small, convenient loads. My chair and table formed one load, fairly light and protective against sun and rain, but not very popular because of the many oddments which were always added to it. Kerosene tins for carrying water (buckets were never used), a few yams for the cook, my raincoat, a plant press (which started empty) and occasionally small packages pushed secretly under cover, containing a boy's cloth, his rations or his sandals. It often resembled a stall in Petticoat Lane and needed expert roping to keep it together.

Rain fell gently as the carriers, having tied their own meagre bundles on to my bulky possessions, helped each other to hoist their loads on to their heads. It took ten of them to keep one white man alive and well in the bush. I could have crammed all their belongings into my tin bath. This was not deliberate pampering of the white man; it was the only way in which he could inspect his District. One night spent as the carriers spent every night in bush, lying on the damp earth protected only by a thin cover cloth, with only a handful of yam and a tiny smoked fish, if he was lucky, in his belly, would have put the average white man in hospital for a month. The carrier was born with malaria in his blood, with an umbilical hernia and worms, and was poorly fed; yet he treated all his afflictions with less fuss than I treated the common cold.

I tailed them down the steep boulder-strewn road which led past the District Commissioner's bungalow, down across the newly made Kumasi-Accra road and for another mile following the road to Juaso New Town station. I tailed them doggedly till we were past the village, knowing that if I led them I should lose them. They would find some excuse to visit the village and half the morning would be wasted. I kept them going across the railway line and along the bush road that goes south to the mud-hutted village of Kusietammu. From thence a footpath led westwards to the eastern boundary of the Dome River Forest Reserve and the steep rounded flank of Dome Hill.

Rain fell steadily as we sloshed through the mud and it continued to fall unabated for twenty-four hours. By the time we had covered the five miles to Kusietammu I felt we had earned a rest. We spent it in the mud-walled village school, talking and smoking while rain drummed on the corrugated iron roof, the local breed of sandflies savaged us, the entire village population gawked at us and a selection of pi-dogs showed their yellow teeth at Robert who yawned his indifference and went to sleep in the only warm spot he could find, on my feet.

The last time I visited this flea-blown hamlet was shortly after the earthquake. This occurred on 21 June 1939 while I was having drinks with Hadow (later Sir Gordon Hadow, Deputy Governor) the District Commissioner and Miller, a policeman. We were sipping our drinks in the comfort of Hadow's lounge overlooking a wide lawn beyond which lay the invisible mass of

Dome Hill. It was 7.30 pm when suddenly an express train appeared to be approaching us from the south-east, an express train, moreover, that was crossing a long steel-girdered bridge at speed. It sounded and felt as though I were in the Flying Scotsman crossing the Forth Bridge. That there was no such bridge in the whole of Ghana, nor express trains, that the railway line was two miles away, did not disturb the illusion. As this monster seemed to be about to tear through Hadow's lounge I noticed with a sudden contraction of fear that the walls of the room were no longer at right angles to each other but resembled a trapezoid. Worse, a trapezoid which moved as though it were about to come apart at the seams. The floor buckled and heaved like a small ship in a rough sea and my stomach with it. Quite without apparent volition we found ourselves standing on the lawn commendably with our glasses firmly grasped in our hands. 'Earthquake,' we exclaimed simultaneously.

When I returned to the forestry bungalow a little later, I discovered the cook quaking underneath the kitchen table in the dark with half the roof and walls about him. I shone a torch on him. 'Massa,' he groaned, 'dis de bad ting.'

I hauled him trembling to his feet out of the debris.

'Earthquake,' I told him succinctly. 'Now what about chop?'

He frowned: 'Massa, I no fit cook chop dis night. My head 'e too trouble me.'

I half-dragged him into the bungalow and gave him two aspirins and a shot of whisky and water. This he downed smartly and tottered away towards his room. At the door he turned.

'Massa,' he croaked again, 'you savvy dat gramophone record that broke?'

I savvied all right! A Richard Tauber record had been smashed beyond redemption. Both cook and steward had denied by all their gods that they had as much as touched it. Now the cook's conscience troubled him.

'It be me broke 'em,' he confessed, miserably, and tottered out into the night.

A few nights later I was sleeping in the Chief's house at Kussie-tammu on my way home from the Mirasa Hills, a Reserve which is still not settled after twenty-five years of wrangling, when I was awoken by drums beating, horns blowing and people shouting. I switched on my torch and looked at the time. It was 1.30 am and I had been asleep for hours.

The bedlam continued for an hour or so and then died. Some juju palaver I thought and slept again.

After breakfast, while the carriers packed the things, I paid my respects to the Chief. I noticed that there were an unusual number of people in his courtyard and enquired the reason. The Chief through his interpreter explained that last night the earth had shaken again. They had all been very frightened and had made a big noise to ward off the spirits. What caused such things, he enquired.

I was young, gauche and striving to make an impression. Off-handedly I explained that probably the gods were angry, possibly because the Chief or his people were up to no good. They had sent the earthquake as a punishment or a warning.

The Chief nodded his head solemnly. 'You felt this thing?' he enquired, blandly. I nodded. There was a little pause. 'Then what,' he retorted, 'had you been doing wrong?'

The courtyard erupted in a roar of laughter. I had the grace to join in.

As we waited for the rain to slacken, the Forest Guard Kobbina Grunshi appeared like a half-drowned green rat, his fez, cape and puttees sodden. He looked as though he had spent the night in the rain. He had in fact been awaiting our arrival since dawn on the Reserve boundary. Whether this betokened praiseworthy zeal or a guilty conscience I could not at that moment tell. He flung back his cape and gave me a salute that would have caused apoplexy in a csm of Ordinance. A pity old Forest Guard Paul Ampofo was not present, I thought. Paul liked to ask permission to drill those Forest Guards who were sloppy in their movements and would sneer openly at any Forest Guard who had the effrontery to appear at the office untidily dressed. In all my service I never knew there to be sufficient uniform for the field staff and sloppiness in dress was often the result of worn and tattered uniforms that should long since have been thrown away. Though drill and an immaculate uniform were not part of the curriculum, a smart and soldierly bearing impressed the people and bred respect, of which we were often shown very little. With little encouragement, however, most

Forest Guards looked impressive at pay-out. What they wore in bush did not matter.

With the Forest Guard so wet and little sign of the rain stopping, I gave the word to load and the laughing chattering carriers set about the business of hoisting their loads on to their head-pads. A well-balanced load was essential if a man was not to develope a cricked neck and it took a few minutes of shuffling about before the point of balance was found. One by one they headed out into the rain, on to the muddy morass which was the footpath out of the village and into the belt of dripping cocoa trees that flanked the path right up to the Reserve. I led, with Robert trailing miserably at my heels.

Robert hated water to the extent that he even flinched when his drinking bowl was filled. He had a monthly warm bath in which he was well soaped and rinsed with lysol in water and deticked. This to him was purgatory and immediately afterwards he would escape if he could to 'shampoo' himself in the pile of wood ash heaped outside the kitchen. From this he would emerge happy and contented in a complete mask of white dust. Rain did not worry him as much, but the wet and mud beneath him were a sore trial to a short-legged dog that was fastidiously clean.

This was a day to get wet and not bother. To wear a raincoat was folly for so high was the relative humidity that although a mac kept out the rain, it also kept the sweat in, the net result being to become as wet as if no protection were worn. We climbed gradually for an hour up the lower slopes of the hill, slipping and slithering in the mud. The carriers were as surefooted as goats and rarely fell. So rare an occasion was it that when Tinga did stumble and fall rolling a tent load in the mud and becoming well spattered with it himself, the boys howled their glee. Tinga grinned and with the help of the Forest Guard collected his load and went on. They were natural comedians and rarely took offence.

As we climbed we entered the cloud which capped Dome Hill and by the time we had reached the boundary line, which climbed steeply almost over the summit, I was sodden and cold. The rain had slackened a little but the air was thick with mist the consistency of wet cotton wool. Under the closed canopy of trees it was almost dark and the world seemed dead. If there should be a hell on earth, a hell compounded of gloom, all-pervading damp and silence, excepting only the sullen drip of water on leaf and loam, and the occasional screech and hoot of an invisible hornbill, the high forest on the flank of Dome Hill on that day was it.

The trees were wreathed in mist and so weighted with water that the air was clammy and cold like a wetsheet encompassing one in shivering embrace. Visibility was about fifty yards; beyond that there was only whiteness. Practically every living creature seemed under the restraining influence of gloom and damp; even the crickets, grasshoppers and cicada were mute; nothing moved and no bird sang. Keats would have loved it. I reckoned that two hours' walking would see us at the top, though it would take the carriers a little longer to catch up. I planned to camp near a hamlet called Mmofrafawjen, about another two hours' walk beyond the hilltop.

The slope steepened considerably as we approached the summit and it was not easy, even unencumbered as I was, to climb without using one's hands. I began to have doubts as to the carriers' ability to continue at other than a snail's pace. It was then about 11 am. An hour or so later we had struggled to the top. From then on it was all down-hill, though I was not sure that this would be much better than the ascent. I sat on the concrete boundary pillar marked FRBP 7, lit a cigarette and surveyed the forest scene without enthusiasm. The rain still fell and the cloud had not lifted. I had never hated the forest so vehemently or wished myself so speedily out of it.

The cigarette, which was damp and tasted vilely, was at last finished; I then gave a loud 'Halloo' through cupped hands in the direction from which we had come. A sustained high pitched 'Hoo' will carry over a mile in still air. There was no response to repeated calls so I began to make a forest inventory in the notebook I carried for the purpose. In this I had recorded all the known slash characters of all the trees I had examined, based on a Nigerian Key compiled by an unknown enthusiast. With the aid of the key it was theoretically possible to identify almost any high forest species. There were always, however, some unknowns which infuriatingly refused to be classified and needed flowering and fruiting material usually not available.

After completing a brief inventory and refreshing my memory I called again. This time there was a faint reply indicating that the van of the carriers was within half an hour's walk. During that period I searched for *Peripatus*. I was to go on searching for *Peripatus* for over twenty years, yet each old log I rolled over, each rotted tree I dug into, might suddenly yield this creature, the first to be discovered in Ghana.

This huge caterpillar-like animal is a link between the lowly worms and the more highly developed Arthropods, that order which contains the numerous, widespread and highly successful insects, crabs, spiders, scorpions and centipedes. Though it is superficially segmented like the worms, these segments bear limbs; it possesses jaws like an Arthropod, but its nervous system is related to that of the more highly developed worms. It is part worm, part 'jointed legs' and as far as I know still undiscovered in Ghana, though occurring in all surrounding territories. By the time I had quartered the area for *Peripatus*, Musa Baz had arrived with the tin bath on his head, trailed laboriously by the Forest Guard.

Musa was a tall (six-foot seven) wand of a boy, still in his 'teens but possessed of great strength and enormous stamina. He was scarcely breathing above normal as he squatted and lifted the bath from his head. The Forest Guard, unladen except for his sodden cape and fez, was puffing like a grampus. When his respiration was more normal he saluted and reported in pidgin English as execrable as my Twi that 'some carrier not fit wakka', and by signs indicated what I had feared, that they were finding it extremely difficult to find footing on the slippery slope. Meanwhile, Musa Baz was on his way back without a word. I followed. We slithered and slipped, clutching at tree stems, weeds, rocks, anything that would brake our downward progress. The rain still came down, steadily, unvaried, as though there were unlimited quantities up above. Half an hour's descent saw the next carrier, Tinga, inching his way upwards, digging his great spatulate toes into the red slippery earth, steadying himself with one hand, while the other kept the sodden tent load on his head. I wished him 'Aye koo', at which he grinned without humour. A little further down we met Musa Moshie, sitting on his tent load. By the look of him he had suffered several falls and his skin, naked but for a loin cloth, was daubed with red clay.

By now Musa Baz was out of sight and the next we saw of him as we continued our descent was on his way up with the third tent load. He seemed to have little difficulty in moving and I stopped to admire the grace of his carriage and the dogged tenacity with which he tackled each difficult little precipice, all now cascading muddy water. The rearguard of the carriers was a pitiful collection of boys, sodden, muddied, and hopeless, or nearly hopeless. For each forward step, they took half a step back and to judge from their woebegone expressions they had little hope themselves of getting to the summit before dark. I was no asset; all I could do was to make encouraging noises, pick up a load when it fell and help the boy to replace it on his head. Thus we inched our way up the boundary.

Even this dismal action was not without its touches of slap-stick humour. John Toe came down mightily, sliding on his backside, followed at slightly greater speed by a full chop-box, like a toboggan rider parted from his steed. At the last split second before the fully loaded box caught up with the luckless Toe, he rolled smartly to one side and disappeared over the edge of a miniature cliff on the side of the boundary. His sudden cry of anguish was stilled as his swift descent was abruptly halted by a conveniently thick bush. As we peered down at the apparently unconscious bundle of muddy rags that was John Toe, he was suddenly galvanized into a series of cataleptic convulsions and his cries split the welkin. The bush was full of vicious red tree ants whose evil tempers had not been improved by the rain. How poor Toe suffered! How the callous spectators, including myself, roared, partly out of relief that he was obviously not badly hurt.

As though deprecating this show of poor taste, the heavens opened and what had been a bearable drizzle suddenly turned into a cold, solid downpour. Then I *knew* we would be lucky if we made camp before dark. It was long after dark when the last exhausted carrier dropped the last load on the top of Dome Hill. By that time Musa Baz had made three journeys down and up the hill, each time with a different load. The rain had not diminished by one drop, and though my tent was up and a tarpaulin erected for the carriers, and a fire was crackling reluctantly, that evening was about the most dismal I ever recall. It was too wet and too late for the carriers to seek the camp where they had intended to spend the night and they grumbled softly together beneath their shelter. It was one night when I really needed a hot bath, but with the realization that it would take hours to heat water on the reluctant fire and that a hot meal was more vital, I had a hot meal instead and like the carriers went to bed dirty. Robert shivered beneath the camp bed but the rolling beat of the rain on the taut outer fly lulled us to sleep. Notwithstanding the damp sheets and cold saturated air we slept soundly till the carriers woke us with their chatter shortly after dawn. The rain had ceased but thick cloud cloaked the hill in a white mantle and we lost no time in breaking camp and slithering our way down hill away from that dripping, damp, depressing dome.

I noted in my daily diary that it had taken the carriers eight hours to hoist my loads two miles up the flank of Dome Hill and wondered whether it was worth it. I wondered what they would have thought if they had known that the only reason I had come this miserable way was to see if the boundary was clean. Clean! I observed that I had once climbed and descended Snowdon carrying a forty pound rucksack, in less time.

CHAPTER NINE

At the Cross Roads

WHEN Timber Thompson described his journey from the high forest near Abetifi, on the mountainous ridge of the Kwahu scarp, to the relatively tree-less Afram Plains, he noted ' the extraordinarily abrupt transition from this type to the dry, open forests of the plains '. Thirty-five years later I constantly marvelled at this sudden change. From the dense, high, semi-deciduous forest with its numerous mixed species on the heights one entered an almost pure forest of low *Talbotiella* trees as one began the descent to the plains. This continued for a mile or so, the descent becoming so steep as to make it just as arduous descending as it was ascending. The fresh traveller going down kept that unpleasant thought out of his mind. As the ground levelled, the air changed from the damp heat of the forest to the almost pungent dryness of the plains, wet skin suddenly dried as though wiped by a soft, cold, dry towel and, magically, it seemed, stayed dry. As suddenly, we find ourselves on the plains, in the open. Ahead of us stretches the grassland with orchard-like trees, rolling in gentle undulations to the horizon and beyond for hundreds of miles.

Thompson followed a more gentle gradient than the one I used years later but we both entered the plains near the village of Nkwantanang (literally ' the cross roads '). At this untidy sprawl of mud huts several hammock paths meet, branching east for Kete Krache in Togoland (now the Volta Region) and west for Atebubu and the main northern trunk road.

For most of the year Nkwantanang houses a few farmers and hunters. There are fewer hunters than in Thompson's time for there is little left to hunt. The huts are the usual mud-plastered-on-poles variety, differing from those in the forest country only by the fact that most of them have thatched roofs. There are three reasons for this: grass is plentiful; it is cooler than corrugated iron or aluminium; it costs nothing.

The village has a small importance lying as it does at a 'road' junction; travellers sometimes halt there after a day's walk across the shadeless plains and spend a night before tackling the strenuous pull up the mountainside which leads to civilization. There were no shops or chopbars in Nkwantanang. It was, as I knew it, a bush village for fifty weeks out of the year. During the remaining two weeks, however, more people, nearly all strangers, could be seen thronging its narrow dirty 'streets' than you would find in Abetifi, the capital town of Kwahu. Every ninety days the squalid, fly-blown village became a centre for a great fetish worship. Thousands made the steep descent to the plains every three months to consult the fetish. They came from all parts of Ghana, and from all walks of life; rich and poor, diseased and well, barren and fertile, old and young. They came to be made well, to have their fertility restored or their potency boosted; they came to seek the secrets of everlasting youth; they came to be made rich; they came also to curse and to lay curses. If you believed the fetish, it was omnipotent and could accomplish all these things for a suitable tribute.

I first heard the drums of Nkwantanang summoning 'the faithful' miles away in the Northern Scarp Forest Reserve. I had been inspecting *Taungya* and the concerted distant talk of the drums was such that I decided to enquire the reason for it at the nearby village of Sadang. There, outside his house, I met a Seventh-day Adventist preacher and his young son. I asked him about the drumming. 'It is the fetish,' he told me, 'the ninety-day Nkwantanang fetish. You need to be cured or to become rich?'

I replied, 'No, not yet,' but his little boy needed to be cured by the look of him. The boy was wan for an African and sat on the red earth nursing his head in his hands, moaning gently.

'He has a headache,' his father said.

'Why not give him aspirin?' I suggested. 'It might ease the pain.'

'We Adventists do not believe in medicine,' he said. 'Faith in God will cure all.'

'You mean you will let your son suffer till God cures him?' I asked.

'Yes,' he replied, 'we rely on God.'

'You are speaking as a man of God,' I told him, 'but not as a father.'

I was angry, but to no avail. His last words were: 'We use no medicines.' With pity in my heart for the suffering boy and contempt for his father, I strode down the narrow path towards the drums of Nkwantanang, summoning those with another faith.

An hour later when I came to the village, the drums were silent, but the sight that met my eyes was one of the most astonishing I had ever seen. In front of the village were thousands of people, lying, squatting, standing, in a vast throng that spread wide over the edge of the plains. It was as though I had suddenly come upon a Cup Final crowd in the wilderness.

As I came closer I saw that the people were ringed around in a rough circle. In the centre I caught a glimpse of a naked woman dancing. The drums were beating again. I eased my way through the dense crowd, my scalp tingling with a sensation I had only once before experienced, but one which I would not easily forget. I remembered the drums then, sounding hollow in the wet of the forest near Dome Hill. It was on one of my earliest treks from Juaso southwards towards the disputed Mirasa Hills Reserve. There in the depths of the forest, rain sheeting down, I caught a glimpse of something white twenty feet up in a tree. I could not believe my eyes when I saw what it was: a porcelain telegraph insulator, the same as we see today carrying telephone wires. I sought about and counted twenty of them, arranged in a line. At some time there had been a telegraph wire strung from tree to tree and I could only presume that they were a relic of the Ashanti Wars with the British.

After a week's slithering in the mud I was on my way home, to the luxury of a long bath and the comfort of dry bed-linen and a sprung bed. We heard the drumming a long time before we reached the drums. In a clearing not far from the footpath I saw a naked girl, white with clay, dancing. We were not particularly welcome, but in deference to the white man (for deference was shown in those days) a chair was brought and I watched the girl dance while the drummers drummed.

She was not yet out of her 'teens, I judged, and was well formed. Her dance, to my eyes, was a grotesque pounding of the feet with knees bent and a quiver of the buttocks. It was not elegant nor was it in any obvious sense sexual. Her face was empty of expression; only her eyes showed either madness of the effects of drugs, or possibly hypnotism. It was some kind of a fetish affair and when I considered we were about to outstay our welcome, I got up, said my thanks, and we resumed our journey. As we headed for the footpath I caught the words 'Na Buroni koo. . . .' (Now the white man has gone.) Presumably they then did something else but what it was I never discovered.

From the Dome Hill to Nkwantanang as the African pied crow flies is less than forty miles, a small distance. In time the two places were separated for me by four years. Fetishes are common enough, they are the religion of the people, and many have their priestesses, so it was with some astonishment that I recognized the Nkwantanang dancer as the same one. She looked much older now, and her once well-formed breasts were already sagging. She no longer wore the same empty expression but her eyes still had the look of madness or drugs in them. Her dancing had improved slightly with the years and she kicked up the dust as she executed little pirouettes. The drummers worked hard, a dozen of them seated on the dry red earth; the late morning sun beat down on their bodies, the drums were cradled between their knees and their hands beat out the age-old rhythm which rhymes with the heart-beat. The white, clay-daubed, naked priestess shuffled and kicked in time.

I looked at the people there. Many of them, like myself, were spectators and some of these were shuffling the awkward-looking steps which typify African dancing. There were clerks and labourers, cocoa buyers in expensive velour hats and lounge suits, farmers in their best cloths, and among them I spotted a green-fezzed Forest Guard as yet unaware of my presence. The people who interested me most were the sick, those whom the European doctor could not cure, those who would not let him cure them; those who could not afford to pay the bribe demanded by the dispenser even to see the doctor; those who could not be bothered to see him, but waited a miracle. There were lepers, syphilitics, children half-eaten away with yaws; there were mad men, mad women, imbecile children living remotely in their own pathetic little worlds, all brought down to the cross-roads by their relatives or friends to be cured by the fetish. Many spoke highly of it, recounting numerous spectacular cures. I wondered at it all.

The drumming and the dancing were a side-show to draw and amuse the crowds, like barkers at a fair. The real business would start with the herding of the 'faithful' about the fetish tree, a gnarled old fig on the outskirts of the village, its bent and twisted roots naked in the red earth, exposed by years of erosion. There the high priest himself, a skinny old man clad in an imposing yet revolting array of skins, skulls, bones, teeth and leather amulets, would issue the red Cola nuts, one to each person. This cost sixpence and gained admission to the 'magic' circle. One nibbled the nut and one was 'in'. Now woes could be detailed to the priest and he would give advice as to how to cure a disease, to double one's money or to eliminate a rival. There were certain conditions, many of them sensible and moral codes of behaviour. Full results were not possible, however, without a suitable 'dash' to the fetish. Many people had brought their 'dashes' with them: a fowl, a goat, a sheep, or money.

The fetish is a thing, an object or a collection of objects with powers to control and exercise good spirits. Two generations ago the fetish would be revitalized periodically by sacrificing a child, slitting its body from throat to crotch, folding back the flesh and applying the still-pulsing organs to the fetish. Now, animal's blood, or even a red watery decocotion of Baphia wood, is used. The priests and priestesses work through the fetishes, calling on the good spirits (there are bad ones too) to help. Blind faith sometimes achieves results; occasionally time solves the problem. At all events the Nkwantanang fetish was a successful, and hence a popular, one. With the thousands attending the fetish it would be astonishing if some good results were not obtained by luck or by faith. The fortunate ones would advertise their fortune. Thus the fetish prospers.

The dancing and the drumming went on past noon, till I was baking in the sun and dizzy with the heat on my bare head. As I moved to go, the still dancing priestess suddenly stopped, turned and ran across to me, her pendulous breasts flapping. She paused in front of me and said 'O Buroni, nante yiye', (O white man, safe journey), and was gone. I wondered if the recognition was mutual.

Writing in 1909 of this locality, Thompson (Report on Forests, HMSO) observed:

Early in the year, when the young grass has just sprung up, after the annual fires have swept over the country, these plains are said to literally teem with game of every sort. With the exception of two herds of buffalo, one hartebeest, one elephant, a few duikers and kob and wart hogs, we saw but little at the time of our visit. The grass had grown high, water was plentiful everywhere, and the game had dispersed in all directions instead of being concentrated in the vicinity of the few pools that contain water in the dry season. Judging from the game tracks met with, elephants and buffalo must be very plentiful. Large numbers of them are slaughtered every year and the flesh taken up to Abetifi for sale. We met numbers of people almost every day who were employed in carrying the smoked flesh to that town. The slaughter of elephants must be great, as one of our guides told me that he had shot ten in one month. Several had been killed just before we arrived in Abetifi. Elephant meat can be purchased almost any day at Abetifi.

While Europeans are obliged to take out licences and are (very properly) restricted as regards the shooting of certain species, no steps whatever have been taken to in any way limit the incessant slaughter carried on by the natives. What the few Europeans out here who care for big-game shooting kill is a mere drop in the ocean compared with the annual bag of the native hunters, yet the only restrictions existing are placed on the former.

To sum up, it may be safely accepted that, with perhaps the exception of the hippopotamus, there is at present no danger of the large game of West Africa being exterminated by the white man. The conditions out here are far too unfavourable for any but the greatest enthusiast to take up in earnest big game shooting as a pastime. The real danger comes from the native inhabitants themselves.

An alternative to limiting the number of native hunters allowed to shoot on the plains would be to take up a portion of the latter as a game reserve and to strictly prohibit all shooting within the area selected.

Thompson wrote sense, but like so many others interested in game conservation, then and now, he over-simplified the problems. 'To strictly prohibit all shooting' within a Game Reserve needed many trained staff and more money than was available until now. Though I defend the Imperialists on most scores, I cannot defend them on this because I believe them to have been timorous and short-sighted. Though they made Game Reserves over thousands of square miles and comprehensive game laws, these were of no value because for over half a century there was no money and therefore no staff to protect the Reserves and enforce the laws.

I covered the ground inspected by Thompson and more besides, and judging from the little I saw—a few antelope and one lion, distantly, I am glad to say—and from recent reports, the 2,000 square miles of the Afram Plains are now game-less. Outside the high forest, with its specialized and comparatively rare fauna, the big game of Ghana is now almost entirely confined to a single Game Reserve, the Mole, in the north. The herds of elephant and antelope, and their associated predators, lion, leopard, hyena and hunting dog, which roamed the plains two generations ago, have gone and cannot be resuscitated. Elephant meat is a rarity and the hunter's profession circumscribed. Thus it must soon be over the whole of Africa outside the protected areas. Even here pressure of population threatens. The control of disease and a higher living standard means a higher birth rate, a lower infantile mortality rate and a greater expectation of life. Within this century parts of Africa, for example, Ghana, which since the beginning of time have had so much land that few even bothered very much about its boundaries, will surely suffer a land hunger. The outskirts of Accra, Ghana's capital, where a decade ago no house or hut could be seen, now boasts regimented housing estates which are spreading swiftly into the *savannah*. Concrete pillars set deep in the soil now mark land boundaries. The pressure on Reserves, both forest and Game, is piling up and it will need strong Governments and an enlightened public to maintain these areas.

CHAPTER TEN

Guarding the Game

BIG game is big money in Africa. Even the smallest game, the forest snail, finds a ready market. Half a century ago, the plains of Ghana, which extend over some two-thirds of the country, teemed with game. Elephant were plentiful and according to Timber Thompson, whose monumental treks took him through the forest and *savannah* of southern Ghana in 1909, elephant meat was plentiful on any day of the week at Abetifi, a hundred miles from Accra, the capital; the southern tip of the Afram Plains where these beasts roamed is less than seventy miles away.

More than one reference has been made to the dancing ground of elephant on these plains and there have been reports of plateaux of elephant dung many feet thick. It is reasonably certain that these, in common with elephant cemeteries, have little basis in fact. Such reports, however, add emphasis to the fact that herds of elephant existed and were slaughtered to the point of extinction by Africans armed with the most primitive kinds of match and flint-lock guns. This happened in our time and within legally-constituted Game Reserves. In Thompson's time the numbers of elephant on the Afram Plains can be gauged from the fact that one of the hunter guides attached to his party stated he had recently killed ten in one month. To kill an elephant with a cap or flint-lock gun is a cruel and often long drawn out business. A bladder shot is commonly used, it is as certain as it is slow and agonizing.

In addition, buffalo, hartebeest, roan, waterbuck, kob, wart-hog and crowned duiker were reported as common. Hunters now too old to pursue game, drooling over their pipes in the villages abutting on the plains, told me that they remember when 'bush-meat dere too plenty'. Asked what has happened to them, they reply sadly 'We chop all!'. Some claim to have killed over one hundred elephant. It is bitter irony that in those days large areas of the

Afram Plains were constituted as Game Reserves, and legislation prescribed that 'Any person who shall hunt, capture or kill in any Game Reserve . . . any wild animal or wild bird, save with permission . . . shall be guilty of an offence. . . .'

The legislation and the Game Reserves constituted by it were a dead letter from the day of enactment; neither funds nor staff were ever made available to enforce the law. In 1960, before I left Ghana for the last time, one of my last jobs was to draft legislation expunging the Obusom-Sene and Onyim-Sene Game Reserves from the laws of Ghana. They had long since been emptied of game, indeed, twenty years ago when I did extensive treks across the plains I saw virtually no wild life. The Colonial Administration, 'the Imperialists', have suffered considerable ill-directed criticism in one way or another. On the subject of Ghana's game, however, little criticism has been voiced, though some is justified. The game, most of it, has gone and nothing except the promulgation of a useless set of regulations was ever done to preserve it. The indifference of the Government is reflected in the views of a pre-war Governor. In 1933, in a letter addressed to the Secretary of State for the Colonies, he admitted that 'I have little or no information as to the game animals which are to be found (in the Game Reserves) and the extent to which they are being destroyed.' This is an extraordinary statement for a Governor to have committed to paper. The District Commissioner in Mpraeso or his opposite number in Juaso, could have given him this information by return mail. Sir Shenton continued: 'I incline to think, therefore, that the existence of the (Game) Reserves give some protection . . . (and) I would not advise that they should be abolished.' Sir Shenton also saw 'no reason for abolishing the close season for birds'. The Game Reserves gave no protection whatsoever and the close season for birds was one of the most fatuous regulations ever conceived and quite inoperable. There was no staff then, nor was there to be any for forty years.

Such official ignorance and indifference achieved what might be expected: the destruction almost to the point of extinction of thousands of elephant, hundreds of thousands of antelope, without consideration of age or sex, in addition to the extinction of their predators who either died of starvation or refused to breed. When I last walked across the Game Reserves of the Afram Plains

H*

I saw one lion and one waterbuck. No wonder the lion looked hungry.

We must regard game in proper perspective. It is pleasant to see and instructive to study. Wild life is an amenity in its own right and we owe it to unborn generations to preserve at least a nucleus of it. In West Africa, where cattle cannot be raised because of the tsetse fly, however, game must serve a more vital purpose than of delighting the eye or instructing the brain. It is for many Africans their main source of meat without which they must starve or emigrate. To preserve game for the sake of preservation, or to constitute Game Reserves haphazardly ignoring the basic wants of the population, is as foolish as to allow its indiscriminate slaughter. Game must be controlled and harvested; there must be laws and trained people and money to administer the laws.

In the forest country, game occurs but it is normally solitary, wary, and hard to kill. The humble snail is a major article of diet. But even the primitive communities of long ago harvested the snail, they did not slaughter it indiscriminately. An annual *Gong-Gong* was beaten and is still beaten, announcing the snail-catching season and drawing attention to the unwritten law that prohibits the collection of immature snails. This is so unusual, and so intelligent an approach to wild-life conservation, that it is astonishing that a similar attitude appears never to have been seriously adopted towards bigger game. Neither size nor sex protects the bigger animals from the hunter's gun, or cruel steel trap. Calves, mothers, mothers-to-be, are killed indiscriminately at all times. The annual hunting fires which draw a moving curtain of flame over thousands of square miles of *savannah* destroy countless animals, many of them babies. The forest hunter must hunt by night with the aid of his headlamp which catches the tapetum of the hunted beast and is reflected, and renders it easy prey for his over-charged gun. The lamp reveals only the eyes of the animal, it distinguishes neither sex nor size. More than one hunter has been fortunate to aim surely when those eyes proved to be those of a big cat, lion or leopard. A few have been not so lucky, paying for their blind intrepidity with their lives.

There are two main vegetation zones in Ghana and though there is a degree of overlapping, each is characterized by its own fauna.

The fauna of the high forest is a highly specialized one. The dominant animal, if we exclude the multiplicity of insect and rodent life, is the forest antelope, the duiker. This derives its name from the Afrikaans word meaning, diver, and is expressive of this animal's mode of running which it does in a series of undulations rather like a land porpoise. The nature of the high forest with its usually tangled mass of shrubs and climbers at ground level has moulded the typical antelope form into a small rounded creature with short slender legs, small neck, slender body with short straight horns or none at all.

The antelope of the plains to survive must be able to run swiftly, hence its long muscular legs and its large barrel-shaped body to house the powerful lungs; it must be able to see its enemies from afar, hence its long neck; and its last line of defence, its horns, must be large. Speed and power it must have. Large size, whether it be of limbs, body, neck or horns, would be a positive handicap in the closed forest. Natural selection over aeons of time has therefore evolved the small, compact duiker, which survives because of its manoeuvrability, elusiveness and inconspicuousness. Whereas the large antelope of the open plains uses its physical powers to escape from danger prompted by eyes, ears and nose, the forest antelope relies mainly on its ears to detect danger and often quiet slow movement to move away from a threat. Air moves sluggishly in the lower layer of the forest and without moving air the power of scent is of little value. Visibility in the forest is often limited to a few yards and eyes also are of little value to the duiker in detecting a predator. It relies on silence, camouflage and, finally, sharp, short, weaving plunges, then silence and camouflage again.

On the plains the predators hunt mainly by sight and scent. For protection the antelope group themselves into herds. In the forest the herd is unknown and even family groups are rare. There is not the substance to sustain a group of animals which must, in the absence of grass, live as browsers, picking a leaf and a fruit here and there. The duiker's camouflage, insignificant size and its silent solitary state foster the illusion that the forest holds little wild life. Often there is plenty, but Man is a clumsy beast and therefore sees little. He kills mainly by the virtue of the hunting lamp at night. Without the lamp Man could not hunt the forest profitably.

In its Control of Hunting Rules, 1936, the Ashanti Confederacy forbade hunting between the hours of 6 pm and 6 am, which in essence forbade the night hunting lamp. Alas, the perspicacity which is shown by native communities in protecting the forest snail by unwritten laws, and *enforcing* those laws, is not extended to the hunting lamp. In the forest country such a law cannot apparently be sustained without a major civic or political upheaval. The Local Authorities realize this. The Government now realizes this. In 1939, the Customs Ordinance forbade the import of ' Lamps which, in the opinion of the Comptroller, are specially designed for the purpose of dazzling animals or birds or otherwise rendering them more easily killed or captured.' This law was repealed in 1953 and I have no doubt that popular demand was responsible.

We assume that the closed tropical high forest is the highest known form of vegetation and consequently that it evolved last. Grass, scrub, tree *savannah*, all presumably preceded the forest in that order. As the latter evolved, the animals of the *savannah* evolved with it, or perished by natural selection.

The chief forest predator is the leopard, rarely seen, even more rarely shot, but quite often heard. Compared with his cousin of the plains he is a much smaller and darker animal, which is what we would expect. The forest serval, a smaller, short-tailed, longer-legged edition of the leopard is much less common, and by virtue of his long legs, this we would expect. Little is known about this animal, but its paler cousin of the *savannahs* can make better use of its long legs and is fairly common.

There are no dogs in the forest; the wild hunting dog hunts in packs and must quarter the plains for its quarry. The success of their hunting is such that few animals can escape; even the lordly lion will succumb to the concerted efforts of the wild dog. They could not operate as a pack in the forest and division into solitary animals would render them impotent. The smaller cats are largely forest animals, for the forest favours the individual especially if he can climb; the golden or sometimes silver cat, the arboreal genet, the civet and palm civet, are all solitary forest hunters.

The honey badger, or ratel, is practically omnivorous like the giant forest hog and red river hog, but while he is a solitary beast restricted to the dry open forest and *savannah* forest, pig, by reason of their omnivorous habits thrive in sounders. Also seen in family groups and companies sometimes are the small mongooses who band together for communal hunting.

There are several herds of forest elephant in Ghana, all to be found within the seclusion of the Forest Reserves. The largest and best known herd, or group of herds, lives in the Kakum and Assin Attandaso Forest Reserves. Little is known of them and they are rarely seen. There are also other herds in the west of Ashanti in the Bia Tano, Bonkoni and Subim Reserves. In the north there are many small herds of *savannah* elephant.

Migratory elephant occur all along the western frontier. These are largely *savannah* elephant which leave the sparsely populated Ivory Coast in this area and regularly invade the lush food farms on the Ghana side of the frontier. Punitive measures are now being taken to control these invaders. Sentiment cannot be allowed to override human economy in such matters and failing recently to disperse them by thunderflashes and drum-beating, the Game staff was obliged to kill an old bull and a cow. This caused them to retreat and it is hoped that they will respect the natural frontier of a line of Forest Reserves that runs close to the artificial Ghana/Ivory Coast frontier. Elephant can be made boundary conscious.

Those in the Kakum and Assin Attandaso Reserves, not far from the coast, are virtual prisoners there, ringed entirely by main roads and railways, but prisoners with ample forest in which to live. Half a century ago, when Ghana was being opened up by railways and roads, these elephants could have escaped into adjacent unreserved forest. Now there is little forest left outside the Reserves and they appear to prefer to remain where they are. Only rarely do they break out.

We speak of forest and *savannah* elephant, and zoologists maintain that they are two distinct species. The plains, or *savannah*, species is appreciably bigger, has bigger ears and tusks. It has four front toes and three hind toes, whereas the forest species has five front toes and four hind ones. Size need not be a specific character: almost any animal changing its environment from the forest to the plains would grow bigger; its offspring would be bigger. The number of toes, however, cannot be altered by a change of environment, and there is no doubt that there are two species of elephant in Africa. Whether there are two species in Ghana is something about which I am not so sure. Recent investigations by the Game Warden supports the view I have long held : that both 'species' have recently been derived from common stock; that not many thousands of years ago when most, if not all, of Ghana was under high forest, there was a single species of elephant. As the forest was destroyed some elephant continued to live in the open areas and the only difference between them and the elephant which remained in the forest is one of size. At my instigation, Dick Chadwick the Game Warden, examined as many forest and plains elephants, dead and alive, as possible, and got his game staff to do likewise. Not one of these was found with the toe character of what is established as a *savannah* species elsewhere; all the animals, and all the tracks examined, showed five front toes and four hind toes.

The elephant living in Forest Reserves must share the forest with the timber exploiter, who is now moving into nearly all high forest Reserves with his men and machinery. Elephant dislike Man as heartily as they enjoy his crops but there is no reason why they should not co-exist so long as the elephants do not become too numerous.

The dependency of the forest hunter on his night-lamp is emphasized by the numbers of elephant which flourish in the Reserves. Rarely is one killed. There are few hunters who will dare to pursue them and if the sagacity of these beasts is true and they learn to live and let live, their future is secure. Fortunately many Forest Reserves are regarded as 'Aban asase' (Government land) and therefore sacrosanct. They are *in effect* Game Reserves requiring no laws and are the zealously guarded perquisites of the Forest Guards who foster this illusion.

In 1945, the Forestry Department, which had become increasingly aware of the ineffectuality of existing game legislation and was anxious that something constructive be done to conserve nuclei of wild life, established a few existing Forest Reserves as Game Sanctuaries in which no hunting or trapping was permitted. The idea was not an ideal, merely an expedient because, as usual, no money was available. It appears to have succeeded and in the six Game Sanctuaries wild life is on the increase.

In the proposed revised Game Laws no attempt was made to prohibit the use of night lamps outside Game Reserves. The main reason is as stated: deny the hunter his night light and he will find no profit in hunting. Although the import of traps with jaws greater than four inches has been prohibited for years, 'man-traps' are made locally from old lorry springs and used throughout the country. The proposed new legislation prohibits the use or *possession* of large steel traps anywhere. More than one man has lost his life through these terrible instruments and much suffering has been caused to the beasts caught in their cruel jaws. Walking along the external boundary of the Awura Forest Reserve, not far from the main motor road running from Kumasi to the north, I once put a walking stick unknowingly into the jaws of one of these hidden machines and nearly jumped out of my skin when the stick was torn out of my hand as though by some hidden savage living agency, as the jaws clashed together. Seventeen of these traps, each big enough to hold a lion, or a man, and each tethered stoutly to a sapling or buried stake, were discovered along the edge of the boundary which is a main footpath, by probing gingerly with a stick. I had each one smashed and left as a warning to the trapper.

Few beasts caught in these devilish machines can escape before death through starvation, driver ants or a gunshot, overtakes them. Lion and leopard do sometimes bite or tear themselves free and the effect on their tempers is such as to render any one of them a man-killer. Man-eating lion, unknown at the beginning of this century, are now so common as to engage much of the Game Warden's time in hunting them down and destroying them. Many have been found to have been injured by a trap.

Another potent cause of man-eating among the big cats is the destruction of their sources of food, the herbivorous game. Tsetse control and organized bands of hunters shooting with automatic weapons and high velocity rifles from jeeps and trucks have wiped out many of the ungulate herds. In order to live the big cats attack domestic animals. These are defended to the best of their ability by the herdsmen with bows and arrows, spears and gas-pipe guns. The cats attack silently at night again and again until either they are wounded, in which case they may become man-eaters, or the herd is destroyed, or the Game Warden can find time to eliminate the predators; 60,000 square miles of territory is a vast area to be covered by one man, who is naturally reluctant to delegate the pursuit of a potential man-eater to a subordinate.

Within the Game Reserves, of which there are now three, control is absolute; trained staff are available and no trapping or shooting or the use of a night lamp is permitted except by special permission. How easily and quickly a Game Reserve can become a sanctuary to a vast assortment of animals is illustrated by the swift success of our major Game Reserve, the Mole. Nine hundred square miles of *savannah* forest uninhabited by man were selected as a Game Reserve in 1956, and although its legal constitution was not achieved until 1958, the Game Scouts by patrolling and discouraging by their presence only (they had no legal powers) any disturbance of the area by fire, cutlass or gunshot, succeeded in attracting numerous animals seeking refuge from the guns of hunters and those of the Department of Tsetse Control which was then engaged in the wholesale slaughter of game.

At this stage the herbivorous game of the northern region was being destroyed at an ever-increasing pace. During the second world war, gunpowder and cartridges were at a premium; there were few imports and both were worth their weight in silver. When wartime restrictions were relaxed, and guns, powder and cartridges were once more freely available, hunting became an organized business and parties of hunters using modern rifles, automatic weapons, searchlights and Land Rovers, set about the business of killing with cold-blooded thoroughness. All over Africa a similar pattern was being repeated *ad nauseum*.

Nine hundred square miles of quiet *savannah* forest was an earthly paradise for many hunted creatures and within two years of its selection the Mole Game Reserve was teeming with game of all description.

In the south, near the sea not far from the capital, Accra, the Shai Hills are a last bastion of the game which once wandered freely over the southern *savannahs*. The rocky precipitous slopes of these hills, some of which rise to nearly a thousand feet above the flat plains, are the final refuge of baboon, leopard, oribi, duiker, and an unusually rich fauna of small mammals, of interest mainly to the zoologist, but worthy of protection nevertheless. A mouse known from the Sudan, which had been found only once before in

Ghana hundreds of miles away, was found again in these hills. For all its lack of inches it deserves protection by the law.

Already in Ashanti the Owabi Waterworks Game Reserve exists. For many years it did not function because of lack of staff; now staff and funds are available it will play its proper part in attracting and conserving small mammals and water birds.

A fourth Game Reserve is being sought in the Western Region to ensure the preservation of the elephant, chimpanzee, Bongo and Giant Forest Hog. The distribution of Bongo, Giant Hog and and the minute Royal Antelope, whose hooves are no larger than a man's small finger-nail, is curious. Although they are found throughout the untouched forest of Ghana and in neighbouring territory, they have not been recorded in Nigeria. The chimpanzee is not uncommon in the rain forest and although the majestic Bongo is not common, it is probably more frequent than its few skins and horns suggest. It is a formidable adversary and is largely nocturnal. It is a proud hunter who can display a Bongo skin cover to the cap or flint of his 'gas pipe' gun; most have to be satisfied with a strip from the similarly striped and more easily hunted bush buck. The Giant Forest Hog is a rare and imposing beast, more than twice the size of the Red River Hog, itself no mean pig, a formidable adversary, not eagerly sought after, and worthy of a place among the protected animals.

From the first wildly enthusiastic but misplaced efforts to preserve game simply by making Game Reserves, in 1909, to the first sober and realistic steps to achieve the same result, spanned nearly half a century. This was time wasted, but not, fortunately, money spent, for none was voted. The first reaction of the administrators to the problem of game conservation was to make Reserves, which they did on a grand scale, and to enact complicated legislation. As Thompson pointed out in 1908, the laws were applicable only to non-Africans and as such were practically useless. The irony of this game muddle was that the Game Reserves were constituted without any difficulty or opposition while the subject of the vital Forest Reserves evoked the most violent reaction among the people.

In 1952 an additional area, the Black Volta Game Reserve, over some 1,000 square miles of *savannah* forest in the far north was constituted, at the instigation of the Department of Tsetse Control. This Department had been created in 1949, and part of its duties was the elimination of the carrier of sleeping sickness in game and cattle, the tsetse fly *Glossina morsitans*. This they attempted to do by the wholesale slaughter of game throughout northern Ghana. The game that got away they hoped would settle in the Black Volta keeping the tsetse fly there away from human civilization. Alas, there was no means of controlling the local hunters and farmers who enjoyed a Roman holiday; there was no Game Warden, no trained staff and no funds, with the result that when finally a Game Warden was appointed and staff obtained and trained in game duties, it was discovered that there was no game in the Black Volta Reserve. It had all been killed and eaten. Those that escaped had fled once again taking with them *Glossina morsitans*. Black Volta : black mark!

The first Game Warden was an ex-Conservator of Forests, A. J. Cox, who was appointed in 1949. Unfortunately, ill-health caused him to resign three years later. Cox was his own Head of Department, though officially there was no Game Department, nor any clear-cut policy. He was attached to Tsetse Control, but since the main task of the latter was the elimination of game, the association did not prosper.

Slaughter by fly controllers and their paid and unpaid local hunters who were often supplied with weapons and ammunition from the Department's large armoury was directed almost exclusively at the herbivorous game, that which shows flight rather than fight. The big predators, which control the numbers of herbivores and keep them within healthy limits (the balance of nature) usually escape; nor is it profitable to pursue them. Poaching also is rife and is terribly destructive. From all over the once dark continent come reports of organized butchering. Because the poacher is in a hurry and cannot be bothered with wounded animals which manage to get away, thousands of animals die slow painful deaths. Because the big predators are difficult to hunt, are dangerous and do not bring high prices for meat or skins, they are rarely molested, indeed they are rarely seen, but the swift decline in numbers of the ungulate herds denies them their right to live. Lion, leopard and serval turn to man and his domestic herds for sustenance.

Cattle-killing, especially by lion, is now common-place in

Ghana. A hungry lion is not only an emboldened beast but a cunning one and the protection of the domestic herds is a constant headache to their owners and the herdsman who are rarely armed with anything more lethal than a spear or a bow and arrow. It is a short step from cattle-killing to man-eating, as is now being demonstrated in Ghana.

Although it has been tried all over Africa where man disputes the space occupied by big game, wholesale slaughter has failed to oust the tsetse fly. Where the herds of antelope have been destroyed or driven away, the tsetse have either transferred their attention to the small mammals, or have followed the survivors. Without the complete extermination of all mammalian life there is no hope of exterminating the fly, for it has been shown that the game-tsetse will live on human blood if there are no animals on which to feed. The problem of *G. morsitans* can be solved by game control. There is plenty of room for both Man and game in Africa if the trouble is taken to conserve the game in proper Reserves whence it can be harvested as any other crop is harvested, to feed the protein-starved African. Game within the Reserves keep the tsetse to themselves. Education is needed here, not only among the Africans who are now rapidly taking full charge of the vast continent, with their numerous herds of useless scrub cattle, but among Game Officers too. This education must begin in the schools.

The departure of A. J. Cox in 1953 left the post of Game Warden vacant and it was not until a year later that it was filled by the appointment of Dick Chadwick, who had been a production officer with the Department of Agriculture since 1951, and had previously been a successful white hunter in East Africa, having shot his first lion at the age of nine! With this appointment a degree of uniformity and organization was at least possible, and the Game Section of Tsetse Control began to play a constructive role in the conservation of wild life, largely because of Chadwick's determination that it should do so.

Chadwick quickly expressed his opinion of the ill-fated Black Volta Game Reserve and strongly urged its abandonment while supporting a proposal for another area. This was uninhabited and had perennial water. Small nuclei of big game had been seen there, it was not too remote, and had ready access by road. The headwaters of the Mole River, a tributary of the White Volta, rise there. This was to become the Mole River Game Reserve. Then in 1957, after almost half a century of muddle, uncertainty and ineffectualness, the subject of game at last came within the control of the one Department best suited to develop it, the Forestry Department.

Forestry and game control are allies, each dealing largely with the conservation of important natural resources. As F. S. Collier, lately Forestry Adviser to the Colonial Office, emphasized after his visit to Ghana in 1954, *the forest will eventually be the only refuge left to the fauna.* Collier considered that Tsetse Control and game control were quite incompatible. He is also one of the few game protagonists who eschews sentiment and in his book *Nigerian Mammals* he states on the subject of Game Protection : ' This is more often than not the subject of much soft-hearted but quite impracticable theory by those who have little or no acquaintance with animals outside zoos and none whatsoever with the difficulties of practical administration.'

Within a year of this change, the Mole Game Reserve was constituted, a Game Protection Officer as well as a Game Ranger recruited, and active steps taken to increase the establishment of Game Scouts and to have them gazetted as established officers, instead of daily rated employees. This is a battle still being fought. Within two years an expatriate Assistant Game Warden has been appointed to relieve the Game Warden when on leave. As soon as possible a Ghanaian will take over charge of the Game Branch as part of the quickening policy of Ghanaianization. In 1959, the whole of the existing game laws were revised by the author and are now in force.

The chief proposed amendments to the rusty Game Preservation Ordinance were the dereservation of the old Game Reserves which had been Reserves in name only, the application of the laws to everyone, irrespective of race, colour or rank, and the issue of hunting licences in accordance with the type of weapon already licensed. This will obviate a great deal of suffering on the part of animals which are so often mutilated but not killed by unsuitable weapons.

We decided that because of the dependence of the hunter on his night light and the shortage of protein in the African's diet it would be unpolitic to ban night lights. On the subject of night hunting the views of a Game Warden are interesting. This is what A. J. Cox, Ghana's first Game Warden, had to say about it:

'The practice of night hunting has increased greatly in the Gold Coast in the past few years (he was writing in 1938) and is a menace to human life and, in my opinion, is the chief factor in the rapid depletion of the stock of game and other animals in the areas where it is carried out.

The hunter carries a lamp on his head and animals, dazzled by the beam, stand. The light is reflected in their eyes and, with this mark, an easy shot at close range is obtained. The usual lamp is a small carbide one with an efficient reflector giving a powerful white beam.

The number of accidents where one hunter shot another or an individual using the path or boundary line forming the hunter's beat led many Native states to pass Bye-laws prohibiting hunting between the hours of 6 p.m. and 6 a.m. In my experience, camping in the bush in many of the States where such Bye-laws are supposed to be in force, the number of gun shots heard during the night hours show how ineffective they are. Accidents are still frequent as there always is the individual who will loose off at any light he sees. A few months ago I was sitting in my tent, pitched on a Forest Reserve boundary line, the time being about 8 p.m. when a shot was fired not more than thirty to forty yards off. If one of my boys had been wandering about as they sometimes do, on their lawful occasions, at that hour he would have been a likely target for the hunter when his eyes reflected the lamp. To warn the hunter that he was too close to be welcome I fired a few shots in the air and, so I was told later, he reached home in record time and swore that some white man, the rapidity of the shots told him it could not have been a fellow hunter, had tried to kill him.

Now to the question of the effect of night hunting on the stock of game. I have it on very good authority (my informant has, I am glad to say, now seen the error of his ways) that an absolute novice straight out from home killed three duiker in the course of an hour or two. The average for a native hunter with a little experience of this form of hunting is believed to be conservatively estimated at six animals per night. It is unfortunate that the females and young are the chief casualties.

Before the introduction of this form of hunting only the man with knowledge acquired after lengthy training was successful as a hunter. Now, armed with a lamp, every possessor of a gun is on a more or less equal footing, and most such men would now appear to indulge in the practice. The old skilled hunter has in many cases given up trying to compete during the daytime, when at night he can treble or quadruple his bag with little effort.

The heaps of spent carbide to be seen at intervals of a few hundred yards on every Forest Reserve boundary line testify to the intensity with which this form of hunting is carried out and the absence of game where it was abundant a few years ago is witness to its deadliness.'

Except in the Game Reserves, enforcement of the Game Laws can never be absolute without a vast army of game officers which no Government could afford to maintain. Laws are easily broken and are not always easily detected; even more rarely can the offenders be brought to book; but these facts are no arguments for abandoning the game laws. An awareness of the value of game conservation is necessary for an appreciation of the need for, and the value of, game legislation. The duty of a Game Department lies not merely in promulgating laws to protect game, nor in enforcing those laws and punishing the lawbreaker. It must inculcate into the public an awareness of the virtues of conservation. When the public is largely illiterate and meat-starved, such education is not easy and cannot be accomplished quickly even if the Government provides the necessary money.

Having secured legislation and the trained staff to enforce it within the Reserves, the Game Warden must now begin the education of the general public. Most effectively this can be done by proclamation as well as by written notification through Local Councils, the Chiefs, the District Commissioners, and through the Ministries of Education and Information. It is easier to educate the child than to convince the adult. The adult hunter, the tough hardened man who takes his life in his hands every time he treads the dark forest, will not take kindly to such education; no matter; it is his sons and their sons who will save the game; save it not merely for the sake of preserving it, but so that it can be harvested regularly and in perpetuity. The forester insists on a sustained yield of timber from his forests and he goes to endless trouble to achieve this most desirable result so that the forest is not overcut and remains perpetual. The yield of game must be controlled in a similar fashion, preserving the young animals until they are old enough and big enough to be killed for meat; to preserve the females until they have produced and raised their young.

Education can be enforced by necessity; for knowledge today, more than at any time in world history, is power. Education can also be achieved through interest. A love of natural history, which is a love of life, can be inculcated in children easily by showing them living things in the process of crawling, running, swimming and flying. Many of the world's most eminent biologists became so because of their delight in living things. The African who has never seen an antelope except in the cooking pot is astonished to see one free, running and jumping; he sees, without being told, that an animal can give pleasure other than via the palate. A poisonous snake can be admired for its grace, beauty and the precision of its killing apparatus. The cats, from the lordly lion to the beautiful little genet, can evoke pleasure in the primitive's mind no less than in that of his educated cousin. Interest begets knowledge.

A man who owns a dog does not kill it when he is hungry; by the same token a man can appreciate a beast without wishing to shoot it or to break its back with a stick. The African's almost instinctive reaction to the sight of a free moving snake is to kill it. More than half the snakes of Ghana (and of the world) are non-venomous and harmless to Man. Tell this fact to an African and he is not likely to alter his attitude. Show him snakes that make no attempt to attack Man and *illustrate* the facts of snake-life and their importance (in reducing the numbers of rodents for example) to Man and you are part of the way to making a hunter more human.

Children, boys and girls, but especially girls, who are the future mothers of the nation, are easy to teach, have a ready interest in wild life and must be encouraged in their enjoyment and knowledge of it. A Zoo therefore is an essential part of a civilized community. In its narrower sense it enables the citizen, young and old, to see the animal as a separate, breathing, pulsing, moving creature, not so very different in some cases from the citizen himself, needing food and water, air and light, love and affection. Whether animals in cages are happier than those in the bush is not the question, and if it were no one could answer it categorically. In cages, properly looked after as they must be in a public Zoo, they serve a useful purpose to the community. In the very least they are educative.

As part of its cultural organization, the Asante Cultural Centre, under the aegis of the Kumasi Municipal Council, has established a Zoological Garden in Kumasi. Here, an ever-growing collection of animals, few of which have ever been seen alive or dead by the average Ashanti, is proving a great attraction, and the sixpences are eagerly paid by adults and children alike to see 'dem bush meat'. Even the hunters who brave the forest at night come to inspect those animals which they 'see' only in the glare of their hunting lamps as a pair of living lights to be extinguished forever with a shot. 'Dat be fine bush meat' said one hardened hunter, his eyes glistening as he appraised a gleaming tubby Maxwell's duiker. 'For bush I go kill 'em!' He made an expressive gesture with an imaginary gun, then sighed as he watched some children attempting to smooth the animal's glossy flanks. 'Dis place be better,' he concluded, somewhat enigmatically, I thought.

A small boy's collection of fishes or tadpoles in a jam jar is not only a small step along the road to manhood and independence; it is a step along the road trodden by immortals: Fabre, Huber, Scott, Fisher and Durrell, men who have made a living science out of wild life and by so doing have enriched and enlivened the lives of all of us. The fate of Africa's fast disappearing game rests with the children of Africa and their teachers, now. Wherever the white man has settled the game has fled. The whole of the Union of South Africa and large stretches of East Africa, outside the Game Reserves and Parks, are almost empty of wild life.

Throughout Africa big game is rapidly on the retreat. The dark continent is stirring as a giant stirs towards the end of his sleep. With increasing emancipation, better medicine, and more healthy babies and a longer life (thanks to the Imperialists) mankind is now swarming swiftly over what was a few decades ago an almost deserted continent. Ravaged by fire and guns, the animals of Africa are on the run. The slaughter is now so concentrated and sustained that there are fears among those concerned with the continent's wonderful heritage of wild life that the critical years have been reached, that extinction faces many creatures. We need not be pusillanimous about killing game; man must kill to live, whether the animals he kills are domestic or wild matters not. What does matter, is not killing, not the manner of killing, but the principle behind it.

The stockbreeder and farmer harvest their animals, allowing the mothers to breed and tend their young and the young to reach maturity before slaughter. The wholesale killing of Africa's game is usually indiscriminate, young and old, male and female die without distinction or compunction. Calves and fawns are killed, or die of starvation at their mother's cold flanks.

Man must eat, but let him eat sensibly, let him harvest the game, to preserve it not only for posterity to eat but for posterity to look at. If education is needed to teach him the best way to achieve this outlook, those in charge of game must also be educated to see and appreciate the viewpoint of the people, to know and understand their traditional attitude towards wild life, and to become aware of the fear that haunts all the people in the distant villages; the fear of starvation because of a lack of meat. Without such understanding and the sympathy which it should engender, all the game staff in the world cannot save the game in Africa.

The Game Reserves will protect nuclei of game for study and pleasure; they will also provide a sustained yield of valuable protein. In nature, a balance is struck between herbivore and carnivore. We must learn how to adjust this balance so that the role of the carnivore is played partly by Man. A big cat may kill once a week, a pack of hunting dogs may pull down a buck every day. We need the cats and the dogs, but not so many of them that they take all available ungulate meat. We must reduce their number and harvest the surplus meat thus available. This is a new conception of Game Conservation in West Africa and before it is practised its principles will have to be studied, not only by Game Officers, but by the new Governments of the new Africa. Game must not only be conserved, it must be harvested, and a nice balance must be struck between the two.

INDEX

Aban asase (Government land), 112, 135, 214
Abetifi, 201, 202, 208
Aborigines Rights Protection Society, 116
Aburi Botanical Gardens, Accra, 32
Accra, 17, 22, 24, 26-8, 207; Club Resthouse, 67; James Town, 26; Plains, 171; Usher Town, 26
'Accra Niggers', 103
Achimota Herbarium, 154
Ackwah, A. E., 112, 115, 117
'Addah Niggers', 103
Adiebeba, 117
Aedes aegyptica, 40
Afram plains, 170, 190, 201, 207, 208, 209
Afram river, 113
African Woods Ltd., 91
Afrormosia, 123, 128
Agogo, 41
Akim Abuakwa, 113, 115
Akwapim mountains, 22
Ammumuniso, 40; Forestry Resthouse, 55, 56, 184; Research Centre, 57
Ampofo, P., 134-5, 195
Andoh, J., 117
Anglo-French Frontier Reserve, 117
Ankasa Forest Reserve, 33
Anopheles, *see* Mosquito
Antelope, 136, 183, 207, 209, 211, 217, 223; forest antelope, *see* Duiker
Apocynaceae, 103
Arnold, P. G., 85
Arthropods, 198
Asafu-Adgye, 138
Asante Cultural Centre, 224
Ashanti, 22, 66, 106, 158, 175, 189; pitsawing industry, 91; Wars, 28
Assin Attandaso Forest Reserve, 213
Atebubu, 201
Atta, Sir Nana Ofori, 113
Aubreville, M., 150
Awesu, J. S. M., 16
Awuni, 191

Awura, F. R., 215

Baboon, 23, 89, 136, 216
Badger, Honey, (Ratel), 212
Baku, 94
Bambila, 191
Bampredasi, 118
Banda, Banda Hills, 38, 41, 132, 189; on trek in Banda, 173-88; Resthouse, 177-8;—Watershed Forest Reserve, 178
Bangor, Forestry school, 80-1
Bannerman, 138
Baphia wood, 205
Basel Mission, 18
Bazabarimas, 132, 177
Bees, beekeeping, 40-1, 95-103; sweat bee, 180
Begoro, 114, 115
Bekwai, 69
Benkumhene, 112-4, 115
Beveridge, I. A., 44, 51-2, 63, 66, 114
Bia Tano, 132, Forest Reserve, 213
Bilharzia, 28, 184
Black Volta Game Reserve, 217, 218, 219
Blackwater fever, 27
Bobiri Reserve, 36, 152; Working Plan, 66
Bongo, 54, 217
Bonkoni, F. R., 213
Bonnie-Apiagye, Forest Ranger, 178, 185, 186
Bontuku, 117
Bosumkese Forest Reserve, 118
Brent, 85
Briscoe, R. T., 91, 121
Brofuyedru, 118
Brooks, R. L., 45-7, 142
Brown, W. T. S., 100
Buffalo, 208
Bui, 181
Burbridge, K., 16, 32, 111
Burnett, Froude, 116, 117

227

Burra, J. A. N., 173
Bush-cow, 183

Cadman, W. A., 82
Cameron, I., 59-61, 156, 182
Canham, P., 45
Cann-Sagoe, P. B., 116
Cansdale, G., 61-2, 64, 67, 70, 88-9, 152
Cape Coast, 28
Cawood, G., 91
Cedar, 23, 94, 128, 148, 170
Celtis, see Esa
Cerebrospinal meningitis, 28
Chadwick, R., 214, 219
Charter, Q. F., 160, 161
Cheetah, 218
Chey, F. K., 70-2, 143
Chimpanzee, 54, 217
Christiansborg Castle, 27
Cicada, 34, 183
Civet, palm civet, 212
Claustrophobia, 27
Cocoa, 17-8, 28, 29, 50, 62, 118-20, 127, 129, 159-62
Cola nut, 29
Coldwells, J., 69
Collier, F. S., 220
Colobus monkey, 35, 40
Combined Operation, 168
Concessions Ordinance, 121-3, 126, 127-8
Control of Hunting Rules (1936), 212
Convention People's Party, 62
Cook, Dr., 79
Cooke, C. H., 116
Cox, A. J., 111, 118, 218, 219, 221-2
Crickets, 34, 181
Crocodile, 183, 185
Culicids, *see* Mosquito

Dahoma, 94, 128
Daily Herald, 75-6
Davies, Dai, 78
Dede Forest Reserve, 112, 115, 116
De Sautoy, P., 100, 103
Devaux, H. E., 189, 190
Di-methyl pthallate, (Dimp), 35
Djabotey, J., 116
'Dogo' Baz, 191, 192

Dome Hill, 189-200, 203, 204; Dome River Forest Reserve, 190, 193
Douglas, A., 65
Dove, tambourine, 182, 183
Driver ant, 136, 215
Duff, Dennistoun, 66, 69, 156
Duiker (forest antelope), 208, 211, 216; Maxwell's, 137, 224
Duncan-Johnstone, A., 115
Dunkwa, 55, 66, 89
Dyce-Sharpe, 97
Dysentry, 28

Earthquake, 193-4
Ebony, 97
Elephant, 136, 179, 183, 207, 208, 209, 213-4, 217
Elephantiasis, 37
Enchi, 54, 56
Epiphytes, 152
Esa, (Celtis), 128, 149
Euphorbiaceae, 103

Fetish, at Nkwantanang, 202-5
Filariasis, 37, 184
'Fire' fly, 40, 184
Foggie, A., 48, 51-2, 66
Fomang Su Reserve, North, 134, 135; South, 117
Forest, 23, 30, 118, 127, 159, 161, 165, 201, 212; cocoa farming, 118-20, 159-63; fauna, 211-5; management, 165-72; structure of, 149-50; temperature, 34; varieties of, 147-9, 151, 158-63
Forest Guard, 85-6, 131-7, 143, 168, 214
Forest Officer, 15, 33, 35, 58
Forest Ranger, 49-50, 131, 137-46, 168, 169
Forest Reserve, 109-45, 159, 161, 163-4; see also under individual Reserves
Forestry, 17, 128, 139, 146-7
Forestry Department, 45-8, 62, 64, 91, 109, 114, 126, 142, 214, 220
Forestry Training School, Sunyani, 59, 141
Forests Ordinance (1910), 109; (1927), 111, 115
Fulanis, 132
Funtumia elastica (rubber tree), 103, 104, 105

Game Preservation Ordinance, 220
Game Reserves, 207-10, 214-7, 220, 222, 225
Game Sanctuaries, 135, 214
Game Warden, 218, 220, 221, 222
Garnett, 85
Genet, 212, 223
Gent, J. R. P., 57, 111
Ghana (Gold Coast), 17-8, 30, 112; education, 137-8; exports, 29; fauna, 210-15; Independence, 62-3
Gibson, W., 97
Glossina morsitans, 218, 219
Gold, 28, 29, 126
Gold Coast, *see* Ghana
Gold Coast Handbook, 32
Grant, G., 121
Grasshopper, 34, 181
Green, G., 16, 35, 57, 85, 111, 118
Grunshis, 132

Hadow, Sir G., 193-4
Haematopata, 184
Harley, M., 65
Harmattan, 160, 161-3
Harper, 44, 63
Hartebeest, 208
Higgs, Bessie, 78
Hodson, Sir A. W., 114
Hog, wart-hog, 208; giant forest, 212, 217; red river, 212, 217
Honey, 'jam', 97-9
Hornet, 41, 185
Hornbill, 197
Horwood, M., 62, 70, 156
Hughes, F. E., 48, 51
Hunting dog, wild, 207, 212
Hwidiem, 117
Hyena, 23, 207
Hypsipila, (shoot-borer), 170
Hyrax, 34, 136

Imperial Forestry Institute, Oxford, 154
Insua, 54
Iroko, *see* Odum
Ivory Coast, French, 23, 158, 213

Jackson, 117
Jamase, 117
Journal of Forestry, American, 52

Juaso, 69, 88, 99, 152, 156, 203, 209; forestry bungalow, 189; New Town, 190, 193
Judd, J. M., 74

Kakum Forest Reserve, 213
Kawle Lagoon, 26
Kebs, 37
Kerr, A., 88
Kete Krache, 201
King-Church, L. A., 16, 43, 47, 57, 85, 111
Kinloch, D., 65, 66, 69
Kob, 208
Kobbina Grunshi, Forest Guard, 195
Kodjo-the-cook, 33, 132, 172, 174, 175, 176, 186, 188, 191
Koforidua, 28, 113
Kole, Sir Mate, Konor of Manya Krobo, 115
Konongo Gold Mines, 98, 99
'Krepi ball', 103
Krobos, 114
Kumasi, 28, 29, 69, 106; Forestry Department herbarium, 154; saw-mill, 91; Timber Producers' Co-operative Society, 92, 106; Town Forest Reserve, 116; Zoological Garden, 224
Kumasihene, Nana Prempeh I, 116
Kusia, 94
Kusietammu, 193, 194
Kwahu scarp, 201, 202
Kyenkyen tree, 94

Landolphia, 103
Land ownership, *see* Concessions Ordinance
Lane, D., 62, 65
Latex, 103, 104, 105
Le Fanu, Dr., 84-5
Leopard, 23, 38, 54, 179, 181-2, 185, 190, 207, 210, 212, 215, 216, 218
Leprosy, 28
Light, photosynthesis, 140, 162; regulating in forests, 157
Limba, 170
Lion, 179, 181, 182-3, 207, 210, 215, 218-9, 223
Littlewood, V., 60
Llandidloes, 82
Llewellyn, Sir R., 80

London, Sir G. E., 114

McAinsh, J. D., 116
McLean, Dr., 88
McLeod, N. C., 16, 32, 85, 111, 116
Macpherson, Dr., 95
Mahogany, 23-4, 30, 94, 123, 128, 129, 148, 167, 170
Malaria, 21, 27, 28, 184, 191, 193
Mamba, 89, 136
Mango fly, 37, 184
Mankrang Offin Forest Reserve, 116
Manual of Procedure, 169
Manyo-Plange, 138
Marshall, R. C., 43-5, 46, 47, 57, 113, 115, 156
Menji, 173, 175, 176
Mepacrine, 40
Miller, W. A., 62
Mirasa Hills Reserve, 194, 203
Mmofrafawjen, 197
Mole River Game Reserve, 207, 216, 220
Mongoose, 38, 213
Monkey, 38, 89
Mooney, J., 65-6, 71, 72, 168
Moor, H. W. ' Bertie ', 35, 43, 57, 111
Mooso, 144, 145, 146
Moraceae, 103
Mosquito, 27, 37, 40, 184
Mpraeso, 141, 142, 209
Mprim, 117
Mramra, 117
Mucuna pruriens, (cow-itch), 39
Musa Baz, 191, 198, 199
Musa Moshie, 132-3, 198

Nigerian Mammals, (F. S. Collier), 220
Night hunting, 210, 212, 215, 221-2
Ninting, 117
Nivaquin, 40
Nkrumah, Kwame, 50, 62
Nkwantanang, 201, 202, 203-5
Northern Scarp Forest Reserve, 202

Obeche, *see* Wawa
Obeng, Forest Guard, 180, 182, 184-5
Obusom-Sene Game Reserve, 209
Odum, (Iroko), 94, 123, 148, 149
Offin Headwaters, 117
Olpidium, major, 79

Omanhene, 113
Onchoerciasis, *see* River Blindness
Onyim-Sene Game Reserve, 209
Oribi, 23, 216
Osumanu, Forest Guard, 54, 56
Owabi Waterworks Game Reserve, 217
Owen, ' Del ', 81
Owusu, M. D., 152, 153

Paludrine, 40
Pamu Berekum Reserve, 117
Para rubber, 104
Peripatus, 198
Perpetual Forest, The, 15, 71, 95
Photosynthesis, *see* Light
Piptadeniastrum, *see* Dahoma
Pitanga cherry, 94-5
Pitsawing, 91, 92-3, 94, 106, 129
Plague, 28
Plants of the Gold Coast (Irvine), 153-5
Plumbaginaceae, 156
Plynlimmon, 82, 83
Ponerine, (black flying ant), 38
Potassium permanganate, 38
Potto, 136
Prah river, 117
Prickly heat, 27, 34

Quarshie, T., 18
Quinine, 22, 40
Quist, 138

Ramsay, J., 72
Ranger, *see* Forest Ranger
Report on Forests . . . Gold Coast, 16, 31
River blindness, 28, 37, 180, 184
Roan, 208
Rowney, L. C., 35, 86-7, 111
Royal Botanical Gardens, Kew, 154
Rubber, 29, 103-4, 105

Sabiya, 177
Sadang, 202
Safo, E. K., 144-6
Sahara desert, 161
Samba, 186, 188
Sandfly, 38-9, 40, 184, 189, 190, 192, 193
Savannah, 158-9, 161, 175, 176, 182, 207, 208, 210, 211, 216, 217
Sawmilling, sawmills, 91, 92, 129, 148

Saxton, S. W., 87, 88, 114
Sekondi, 28, 29, 86
Serval, 38, 212, 218
Shai hills, 23, 216
Shea Butter tree, 176
Shingle-cutting, 105
Simulium fly, 37, 180, 183-4
Slavery, 63
Sleeping sickness, 184
Snail, forest, 208, 210
Snakes, 139, 223
Soil, 119, 170-1
South Wales Echo, 75;—Football Echo, 75
Steven, H. M., 81-2
Stevenson, D., 46-7
Stock-map, 165-7
Stool, the, 29, 30
Streptogyne crinita, 192
Subim, F. R., 213
Sunyani, 69, 99, 100, 118, 142, 173, 181, 185; Learners' Training School, 59, 141
Surveying, 165
Swollen shoot, 160

Tabure, 117
Takoradi, 45, 167
Talbotiella tree, 201
Tamale, 28, 88
Tampuri, 191
Tano Nimdi Forest Reserve, 144
Tano Offin Reserve, 116
Taungya (forest farming), 168-70, 202
Taylor, C. J., 65, 69, 70, 89, 149
Teak, 171
Terminalia superba, see Limba
Thomas, L., 77
Thomas, Sir S., 209
Thompson, H. N. 'Timber', 16, 17, 21-32, 57, 85, 110, 111, 147, 149, 201, 205-6, 207, 208, 217
Timber, 29, 214; industry, 120-29, 167; pitsawn, 91-3, 106
Timber Lands Protection Bill (1959), 124-5

Timber Protection Ordinance, 30
Tinga, 191, 198
Toe, John, 191, 199
Tolmie, G., 52-7
Tombe stream, 175, 186
Tonicle, The, 81
Trans-Volta Togoland, 171
Traps, for Game, 215
Trees, 146; enrichment planting, 158, 169-70; enumeration and identification, 151-6; growth rate, 150; measuring, 168; Nourishment from soil, 162; plantations, 170-1
Triplochiton, see Wawa
Tropical Shelterwood System, 151, 157
Tsetse fly, 36-7, 183-4, 215, 218, 219; Department of Tsetse Control, 216, 217-8, 219, 220
Twi language, 152, 153

Umiker and Fluekiger, 55, 121
University College of South Wales, 77-8
Useful Plants of West Tropical Africa, (Dalziel), 153, 155
Vigne, 35, 44, 47, 65, 111, 113, 156
Volta river, 158, 175, 179, 181, 182, 183-5, 220; Black Volta Game Reserve, 217-8

Waterbuck, 208, 210
Wawa, 23, 93, 128, 149
Wax moth, 99
Wenchi road, 173-4
Wenman, 69-70
West Indian Cigar Box Cedar, 170
Western Mail, 75
Wewa, 175, 186, 187, 188
Wiawso, 66
Williams, K., 78
Wills, 'Helen', 35, 44, 70, 89, 90-1, 106-7, 111
Working Plans Branch, 157

Yellow fever, 27, 184
Yoyo Reserve, 54
Ystradgynlais, 76